THE OVERNIGHT MILLIONAIRE

WHAT CAN HAPPEN WHEN
SOMEONE KNOCKS ON YOUR DOOR

JENNY GOU & STEVEN LOUIE

BEYOND
PUBLISHING

Quantity sales special discounts are available on quantity purchases by corporations, associations, and others. For details, contact the publisher at the address above.

Orders by U.S. trade bookstores and wholesalers.
Email info@ BeyondPublishing.net

The Beyond Publishing Speakers Bureau can bring authors to your live event. For more information or to book an event contact the Beyond Publishing Speakers Bureau speak@BeyondPublishing.net

The Author can be reached directly at BeyondPublishing.net

Creative contribution by Lyn Smith
Cover Design - Low & Joe Creative, Brea, CA 92821
Book Layout - DBree - StoneBear Design

Manufactured and printed in the United States of America distributed globally by BeyondPublishing.net

BEYOND

New York | Los Angeles | London | Sydney

ISBN: 978-1-63792-315-3 Hardcover
ISBN: 978-1-63792-316-0 Paperback
Library of Congress Control Number: 9781637923153

CONTENTS

DEDICATIONS

To my husband Ronnie who has supported me in everything I've done from day one. My kids, they are my why and reason for everything I do. To my mom who taught me the importance of hard work and giving back. **Jenny Gou**

***

To my lovely wife Rebecca who inspired and pushed me through this journey of life.

To my two daughters who have grown up to be loving, confident and strong young ladies.

And to my parents who instilled the value of GOD and family within our lives. **Steven Louie**

***

And to all of our investors, partners, and friends in the business. This is a team sport and we appreciate the support and trust you have in us.

Jenny Gou and Steven Louie

PROLOGUE

We've all seen this quote out there from Andrew Carnegie. *"Ninety percent of all millionaires become so through owning real estate."*

What did all these people know that we, the common folk, didn't know? And how did they get started? Only the super wealthy and institutions are able to invest. True? I'm too old to start investing, it won't make a difference now. Right?

Nope. Investing is available to everyone and the next best time to start is now (yesterday was better).

Anyone can invest in real estate, and you don't have to live on instant noodles for ten years to get started. Quite frankly, we wish someone had told us about the benefits many years ago.

That's why we wrote this book. We've learned a lot in our journey to financial independence and today live a #lifebydesign. To inspire others to start thinking about this new opportunity, we penned an easy-to-read novel and provide a different take on why apartment investing is our vehicle of wealth.

This is not your typical finance self help book. We think you'll actually enjoy reading this.

Enjoy the book - and if you do - make sure to share it with your friends and family so they can be part of that 90% from above.

CHAPTER 1

Katherine opened her eyes, checked the time on her phone, and gasped. It was 7:00am, and she had overslept her alarm by an hour. She jumped out of bed and rushed to check on six-year-old Zoey, who was still sleeping soundly in her bed. Katherine pressed a soft kiss to Zoey's forehead and gently shook the girl awake.

"Sweetie? It's time to get up or we're gonna be late," she said.

"No," Zoey replied, groggily before pulling the blanket over her head. "Don't wanna." The girl wasn't an early riser. In fact, she was the exact opposite; she was a born night owl. Just like her daddy. Jake always said it would be easier to wash the spots off a leopard than blast their little girl out of bed in the morning when she didn't want to move.

Jake. A lump formed in her throat as she thought about her late husband. She ran a loving finger over his wedding ring, which she wore on a chain around her neck. It had been a year since his passing in a car accident, and she still felt like life was blurry and out of focus without him. Even worse, these days, she felt like the hamster on a treadwheel: Same routine every day. Get up. Go to work. Take care of Zoey and the house. Go to sleep. Get up the next day and lather, rinse, repeat.

Katherine snapped herself back to reality. She didn't have time for reminiscing. Besides, if she gave into the feeling, she might just crawl back into bed, herself, and stay there. But she couldn't do that today. She rushed through Zoey's closet and dresser to find school clothes. "Sorry, my love," she said. "You have school today and I have to go to work." She tossed a pair of jeans and a long-sleeved tee-shirt on the end of Zoey's bed. "Up and at 'em, kiddo."

Katherine went back to her room and rummaged through her own closet. She had to make a good impression because today was a big day at work. It was the Bright Futures Board of Trustees annual strategic meeting where the entire year's fundraising and strategic plans would be decided, and she was the executive assistant to the president of the non-profit. She couldn't be late today, and she had to make a good impression.

She settled on a smart pencil skirt and fitted blazer in navy blue, paired with a white Oxford shirt. Simple. Classic. Elegant. Ten minutes later, Katherine was dressed and rushing to get milk and cereal on the table. There was still no sign of Zoey and no noise from upstairs. Usually, when there were all sorts of noise coming from upstairs.

"Zoey?" she called out. "Let's go, honey. Mommy has a busy day at work today."

Zoey trudged down the stairs. She was mostly dressed, and the tee-shirt was even on the right-side out. She hopped on one foot as she struggled to squeeze her foot into her sneaker. "I can't get this on, Mommy," she said with a dramatic sigh as she plopped down in the middle of the floor. "Why are shoes so hard?"

"Let me help," Katherine said, sitting down on the floor next to her daughter. She loosened the shoelaces and then wiggled the sneakers onto Zoey's feet. "Ok, eat breakfast, please. We need to get going or I'll be late for work."

She poured milk and cereal for Zoey and grabbed a banana from the fruit bowl for herself. After making sure all of Zoey's homework assignments were in her backpack, along with some snacks for lunch, they finally got out the door.

The school wasn't far from their three-bedroom apartment, but the side streets of their small Chicago suburb were already congested with traffic. Katherine kept an eye on the sky because the clouds had grown dark, and it was threatening rain. By the time Katherine dropped Zoey off at school and got back in the car, the skies opened like someone had turned on a massive firehose in the sky.

"Can it just not rain today?" Katherine said out loud. "Is it too much to ask?"

She tapped the screen on her phone and checked the traffic report. After seeing the gridlock on I-94 into Chicago, made worse by rain that should only be navigated with a huge ark carrying a literal boatload of animals, she was tempted to give in to more self-pity. Instead, a flash of inspiration hit her courtesy of a METRA billboard that read: Was METRA an option today?

The train station was only a few blocks up the road and, if she hurried, she might make the eight o'clock train which, with any luck, would get her to work with a few minutes to spare. She pulled into the parking lot of the train station, paid for the parking slot, and raced to the train platform. Katherine made it onto the train right before the doors closed.

She sank into the first available seat and heaved a sigh of relief. It was a good thing she had prepared so thoroughly for the meeting the day before. Suddenly, she was as exhausted as if she had just run a marathon. *There has got to be more to life than this*, she thought.

***

Wilson Devereaux sat calmly at the conference room table, steepling his fingers as he stared intensely out the window at the city's skyline. He was immaculately dressed in a three-piece suit—Armani, of course—and his snow-white hair was perfectly coiffed. His face was worn and weathered. Even his wrinkles had wrinkles, and he had earned every single one of them.

At eighty years old, he didn't much mind the way he looked. In fact, except when his arthritis flared on cold, rainy days—like this one—he usually felt like a much younger man. Not today, though. Right now, he felt the weight of mortality pressing down on him.

"Wilson, so glad you're here," a booming voice called out from the doorway.

Wilson turned toward the voice and, when he saw who it was, smiled and rose from his chair. "Peter, so good to see you," he said, extending his hand. Peter Monroe was the president of Bright Futures, one of Chicago's most beloved non-profit organizations, famous for its support for small business owners and their needs. They had been friends for nearly twenty years.

"And it's good to see you, buddy" Peter replied, shaking his old friend's hand. "Ready for another fun-filled day of strategic planning for the next fiscal year? I hear Sarah has a slam-bang icebreaker activity to kick us off today."

Wilson groaned melodramatically. "I think I'd rather have a colonoscopy than sit through another one of Sarah's icebreaker exercises. She better not have a trust fall planned for us. I could break a hip."

Peter laughed. "I do love that quick wit of yours, Wilson. If there are any trust fall shenanigans planned, you're absolutely exempt from participation. Anyway, I thought I'd check in to see if you need anything before the meeting begins."

"If you were a genie, I'd ask for another twenty years to do more good in the world."

"That's quite a statement. Everything ok?"

"Oh, yeah. I'm fine, but...don't you wish you could do more in this life?" Wilson said, looking out the window, again, with a wistful look. "To have more of an impact on the world with what we do, I mean?" Wilson noted his friend's furrowed brow and hastened to add, "It's not that we don't have a positive impact on small business owners who work with Bright Futures because I know we do."

"We do, indeed," Peter replied. "I do sense a 'but' coming that caveats everything you just said."

"Not 'but', really," Wilson said." It's more of an "and" statement. We have a great impact on the small business community in Chicago and—see what I did there—we could do so much more."

"You're in a philosophical mood today," Peter replied., Concern clouded his eyes. "What's going on, buddy? You're not sick, are you?"

Wilson waved him off. "Nothing like that. Just the musings of a man who wants his golden years to count for something."

Peter gave his friend a skeptical look. "If you say so." He paused, then said. "I'll leave you to your musings, then. I have a few more things to check before the meeting begins. I need to check in with my assistant, Katherine. She's running all the logistics for the trustees' meeting, and I want to make sure we're ready to go."

"Go on, I'll be fine here on my own for a bit."

A few minutes later, a young woman joined him in the conference room. She began arranging the danishes, fruit, and breakfast sandwiches on the refreshments table. Then she moved on to the bottles of water along with little packets of sweetener and creamer, napkins, stirrers, lids, straws...the whole works. Also, on the table were two tall, silver coffee urns, the sharp scent of dark roast filled the air.

"Now this is how you do it." Wilson gave the woman a thumbs up as he walked over to pour some coffee. "Executive assistants run the world."

"That's why we get the big bucks, sir" she said, checking to make sure everything was in place.

He laughed and opened one of the little creamers and poured it into his cup. "The big bucks, indeed. I'm Wilson Devereaux," he said, extending his hand to her. "And who might you be?"

"Katherine Johnson, sir," she said. "I'm the executive assistant to Bright Futures' president, Peter Monroe."

More staffers came in and double-checked the projector and laptop computer used for the presentation. Then two other admin assistants came in with photocopied handouts. Katherine took charge and began assigning roles and tasks.

Wilson watched her, impressed by how organized she was, and the rapport she had with every member of her team. He began thinking about the program he wanted to start to help people learn how to invest their money. Perhaps Katherine Johnson was the perfect candidate to help him get the program and running.

"I love the guy who owns the EPIC Bounce playground over on Fourth Avenue. He is so creative," a woman named Marissa said.

"I know that business. Brian McMasters owns it. That's the place with the huge inflatable obstacle course." Katherine said. "My daughter loves going there. They do great birthday parties."

"Yep, they do," Marissa replied. "That business is exploding. Most of the time, you must reserve play time at least a week in advance to get a spot."

"He's doing a wonderful job growing the business," Katherine replied. "He's in the process of building a franchise model for the indoor playgrounds. But what I love most about him is that he is so humble, and has a great work ethic. He's not afraid to roll up his sleeves and help his staff with any of the work."

"Right?" Marissa replied, "I was there with my kids one Saturday, and he was emptying the trash because one of his employees called in sick."

"That's what you have to do when you're a small business owner," Katherine said. "It's all about dedication and commitment. And loving what you do."

Wilson approached her and said, "You seem like someone who understands what it takes to be successful. You also seem like a woman who wears many hats with ease, Ms. Johnson," he said. "In fact, it looks to me like you could run this place single handedly."

Katherine seemed taken aback by his compliment. "Thank you, Mr. Devereaux. That means a lot coming from someone who has helped so many people over the years. You're quite a legend around here."

"Please, call me Wilson." Looking around the room, he asked, "Are you always this well prepared? And you seem to have a passion for small business owners. If so, I think we can work together."

"Work together how?" She asked, giving him a quizzical look.

"There's something I want to start to help people learn how to take control of their finances, and your skills in organization will be an asset."

She smiled at this. "I'm not sure I'm who you're looking for. I have a lot on my plate right now."

"How about this," Wilson said, "just come by my office tomorrow and we'll talk about it. Maybe we can figure something out."

"My late husband used to say it costs nothing to have the conversation," a wistful look clouded her face for a moment, then cleared up and she smiled like the sun had just emerged from the clouds.

"Late husband? Oh, I'm so sorry." Wilson gave her an empathetic smile. "Do you have children?"

"Yes, a little girl. Zoey. She's six-years-old."

Wilson gave her a gentle, understanding smile. "I'll bet she's a handful. I was never blessed with children."

"She is definitely a handful." She laughed. "I appreciate the invitation to meet with you but I to warn you, I really like what I do here at Bright Futures."

"I understand completely. It's important to have a passion for what you do, to have more of a vocation than just a job. You never know, you might enjoy a change of pace."

Katherine nodded and took the card he held out to her. "All right, Wilson, I'll come see you tomorrow."

"Great," he replied. "I think you'll find this opportunity hard to resist."

CHAPTER 2

K atherine drove her sedan up a long, tree-lined driveway. She could see the white stucco exterior of Wilson Devereaux's mansion sparkling through the trees. She tried to breathe deeply so she could relax. Katherine had no idea what to expect. It wasn't every day she was invited to a job interview by a millionaire. Actually, she had never been invited to a job interview by a millionaire.

She parked near the end of the driveway and was surprised when a valet tapped on her window and asked for her keys. Apparently, when you're a millionaire, you can hire valets for your house to park cars. Katherine ran a comb through her hair one last time, checked her teeth in the review mirror— no lipstick, good—and grabbed her laptop bag.

The valet directed Katherine through a garden that led to the rear of the house where Wilson Devereaux's offices were located. The garden leading to the back of the mansion looked like it belonged at Versailles—it was bordered by meticulously-trimmed hedges that separated it from the rest of his vast property. In the middle of the garden was a wide lawn that stretched out to dozens of flowerbeds filled with roses, tulips, daffodils, daisies; so many other varieties,

Katherine couldn't count them all. The entire garden was awash in color and the scents of roses and jasmine and honeysuckle.

The door opened before Katherine even knocked. A man, presumably a member of Wilson Devereaux's staff, greeted her. "Mr. Devereaux is expecting you, Ms. Johnson," he said. "Please follow me."

The staffer led Katherine through the corridors of the mansion and ushered her into Wilson's office. It was a spacious office with an inviting masculine feel to it. The walls were wood paneled, and floor-to-ceiling bookcases lined one wall. Large windows looked out onto the South part of the lawn and into the gardens. There was so much natural light streaming through the windows, the entire room was filled with a golden flow. Wilson rose from behind a huge oak desk when she was announced.

"Ms. Johnson, I'm so glad you're here," Wilson said, crossing over to her and clasping her hand in both of his. "Please, have a seat. We have a lot to cover." He turned to his staffer and said, "Rick, would you ask Mrs. Porter to bring the afternoon tea in for us, please?"

"Of course, Mr. Devereaux," Rick replied, and closed the office door behind him as he left.

Katherine settled into a plush leather wing-back chair in front of Wilson's desk. "You said you have a job offer for me?"

"I do. But it's more than just a job offer. It's an opportunity to help change people's lives. I have an idea for a new program, a way to help people learn the importance of growing their wealth," Wilson said. "I'm going to invite five people to submit proposals for what they would do with one million dollars; how they would invest a very large sum of money to increase their wealth. My goal is to help them learn the value of growing their money to realize their dreams. Each person who makes it through the vetting process will receive one million dollars."

Katherine's mouth dropped open, and she blinked several times trying to take it all in. "Seriously?"

Wilson chuckled. "Yes, seriously."

Katherine let out a low whistle. "That's quite generous, Mr. Devereaux," she said.

"Remember, I asked you to call me Wilson," he replied. His smile turned to a quizzical look. "You're wondering why I would do something like this, aren't you?"

"Well, yes. I mean, you're planning to give away some serious money. You already have philanthropic work through Bright Futures and, I'm sure, other organizations. So why this? Why now?"

Wilson laughed. "I know I may not look it, Ms. Johnson, but—"

"Katherine, please," she said. "Since we're on a first name basis now."

"Ok, Katherine," Wilson continued. "I know I may not look it, but I'm not a spring chicken anymore." His pale blue eyes twinkled and the wrinkles around his eyes and mouth puckered up a little more when he smiled.

"Oh, I don't know about that," Katherine said. "You look spry to me."

"Spry." He chuckled. "Well, thank you for that. But when you get to be my age, you start thinking more about your legacy and less about how many cars are sitting in the driveway. I have no heirs, Katherine. No one to give the fortune to. Sure, there are charities that will receive a handsome endowment when I leave this earth but that's not enough. I don't expect to live forever, you know, but having all of my money disappear into the coffers of an institution isn't what I want either."

"So, you want to give some of it away to help people have better lives?"

"Not just that. I want people to learn how to invest. Did you know that 25 states in America introduced legislative bills in 2021 to require personal finance classes for high school kids?"

"No, I didn't know that. It's pretty impressive, though."

"Not impressive enough. That's only half of the states in the union, and the legislation hasn't yet become law. Not to mention, only seven states already have personal finance classes in already in their curriculum. Only seven. And we have several generations who never really learned the value of investing money. I want to help change that. Well, for a few people, anyway. And, who knows, this could grow into a bigger program, a movement to help people help themselves."

"I understand," said Katherine. "But this is quite a responsibility too..." She paused for a moment then continued carefully. "You'd have to pick the right people to be in your program."

There was a knock on the office door. Mrs. Porter and an assistant brought in a serving cart laden with food.

"I hope you're hungry," Wilson said. "I spent several years in England and got into the habit of having afternoon tea. It's a nice Pick-Me-Up in the afternoon."

"I'm starving, actually," Katherine replied. "I skipped breakfast this morning."

They sat down to a small feast of tea cakes, scones with clotted cream and strawberry jam, and finger sandwiches. The assistant set up the serving ware on the table between them, and Mrs. Porter poured the tea from a teapot that looked like Queen Victoria might have owned it.

"Thank you, Mrs. Porter," Wilson said. "It all looks delicious."

Mrs. Porter and her assistant excused themselves and went back to their work. After they left, Wilson continued.

"Now, back to what I was saying," Wilson said. "I want to find people with good business acumen but, more than anything, I want people with passion for what they do, folks who have a real fire in their belly to succeed and grow their money. I want people who are willing to work hard and have the strength of their convictions on even the toughest days."

"All admirable traits," Katherine said before biting into a fresh scone with clotted cream and jam. "You must have financial holdings all around the world, so why give away money when you could invest it somewhere else?"

"Oh, trust me, this is an investment. It's an investment in people."

"I want to give the money to people who will put it to good use. If they invest it right, take some calculated risks, they should see a pretty good return on their investment."

"I'm looking for someone to help me find the right people to apply for the program." He took a sip of his tea and watched her. "I think you're exactly what I'm looking for, Katherine. You seem like someone with an entrepreneurial spirit—and that's what this program is all about."

"Why not just run an online ad or film a commercial?" She asked him. "You could get a lot of applicants for your program."

"That's not the way I do business." Wilson took a bite of his sandwich and chewed thoughtfully for a minute or so. "I like to do business one-on-one as much as possible. I like to get a feel for who I'm working with. Figure out what makes them tick. And you, my dear, have the sort of passion and dedication I'm looking for. You love small business owners and I have a feeling you have great instincts when it comes to reading people."

"I am pretty good at reading people," Katherine said. "I'm very flattered that you want me to join your company, Wilson. Truly, I am. And I don't want you to think I'm ungrateful, but I did tell you, yesterday, that I'm very happy as an executive assistant at Bright Futures. I'm not looking to move."

"And I'm not looking for an executive assistant," Wilson's eyes twinkled. "I want you to be my program director.

Katherine's heart beat faster. She knew she needed to say something, but her tongue felt like it had swollen to twice its size.

"I really appreciate your confidence in me, but I'm not who you think I am. This whole program director thing is too much responsibility for someone like me to handle." Katherine was gradually aware that Wilson had fallen silent beside her.

"Don't say that Katherine," he said. "Don't ever think of yourself like that. You may doubt your abilities, but I do not. You can run with this program. You can help make a difference in people's lives. That's why I want you there with me every step of the way."

Katherine looked into Wilson's eyes, and she saw only warmth and sincerity. She wished she could be more like him, not questioning herself at every turn. Perhaps given time, this job could work out. Perhaps one day soon she would believe in herself the way he believed in her. But for now, she didn't believe she could do it.

"I can't," she said after a pause. "I am so incredibly flattered, Wilson. I would love to work with you and develop this program. But right now, you need someone who can hit the ground running. I'd be devastated if I let you down."

Wilson leaned forward in his chair and looked her straight in the eyes. "Katherine, you will not let me down. I have faith in you."

Katherine felt his blue eyes bore into hers and instinctively she wanted to look away, but then she thought it would be rude. She didn't want to hurt his feelings by turning down the offer he'd made her. But at the same time, she couldn't give him false hope either. If she said yes, and then failed, it would be worse than just turning the job down in the first place.

"I'm sorry, I just can't right now."

Wilson watched her in silence for a few minutes before speaking again. "I understand how you feel. I won't push any harder right now, but I want you to know the door is always open for you. Please just think about it. If you change your mind, let me know."

***

Katherine couldn't get the conversation with Wilson Devereaux out of her head as she drove to her parent's house for dinner that evening. Had she made a mistake in turning the job down? She was nervous, and she didn't want her family to see it. She took a deep breath to steady herself. Zoey sat in the backseat of their car, reading a book to pass the time while they drove.

"We're here, sweetie," Katherine said, as she pulled into the driveway. "Are you excited?"

"Uh huh," the girl replied. "I can't wait to see Grandpa and Grandma!"

Katherine unbuckled herself quickly and jumped out of the car to open Zoey's door for her.

"Mommy, you don't have to help me. I can do it," Zoey protested as Katherine shoved her seat forward and tried to lift her out of the car.

Katherine laughed and shook her head. "You are getting to be such a big girl, aren't you?" She took a deep breath and reminded herself to let go of some of the nervousness she was feeling before they entered the house.

"I'm glad you're on time for once," came a voice from behind them as Katherine and Zoey started toward the door. "You're always late for family dinners."

Katherine forced a halfhearted smile and said, "Not always."

"Yes, always," Deirdre said with a roll of her eyes. "Why do you think we joke about Katherine Standard Time? You're always in your own little world." Laughing to herself, she walked on ahead to knock on their parents' front door while Katherine and Zoey followed quietly behind her.

"Come in," came their mother's voice from inside. Deirdre opened the door and gestured for them to enter first before following them inside and closing the door behind herself.

"It's so nice to see you all," mother said with her usual fake sincerity as she set the table. "Think you could give me a hand getting dinner on the table?

"Sure, Mom," Katherine said, as she headed to the kitchen to grab the serving platters of food.

As Katherine's father took her coat from her, he kissed her cheek politely. "You look tired today."

"Thanks, I guess," Katherine said, feeling wounded.

Deirdre talked about the new project she was working on for most of dinner. It seemed like her job really did spark a sense of accomplishment within her, and Katherine felt a pang of jealousy at how quickly Deirdre had been able to bounce back from her divorce. Her sister had always made life look so easy.

"How are things at the law office, Dee?" Dad asked. "Getting along, ok?"

"Things are great. I met with a new client today," Deirdre said, spearing a piece of chicken. "The partners are so pleased with my work that I pretty much get the first choice of the really interesting, high-profile cases."

"That's wonderful, dear," Mom said. "What about you, Katherine? How is work going? Are they giving you more responsibilities at Bright Horizons?"

"Work is fine, thanks," Katherine replied. "We had a Board of Trustees meeting yesterday that went pretty well."

"Sounds exciting," Deidre said with a smirk.

"Actually, it was," Katherine said. "I met Wilson Devereaux at the meeting."

Dad perked up, suddenly interested. "The real estate tycoon?"

"Yep, that's him. And he asked me to meet with him today."

"Why in the world would Wilson Devereaux want to talk to you?" Deirdre scoffed.

"Dee, don't be rude, dear," Mom said.

"Well, what happened?" Dad asked. "What was the meeting about?"

"He's starting a program to help people learn the value of investing their money. Long story short, he wants to find five people to submit a proposal describing what they would each do with a gift of one million dollars."

"Is it a fundraiser for charity or what?" Dad asked. "Millionaires are always doing things like that. Giving money away and then reaping the good publicity."

"Don't be critical, Richard, it's a lovely thing for Mr. Devereaux to do," Mom said. "After all, he has the money to do it, and there are plenty of good charities who could use a windfall."

"No," Katherine said. "It's not like that. He's not doing it for the publicity. He genuinely wants to help people learn how to grow their wealth. Too many people don't know how to make the most of what they have. He wants to change that."

"You don't mean to say he's actually giving away a million dollars," Deirdre said, sounding shocked. "Where do I sign up?"

"Mommy," Zoey piped up between mouthfuls of chicken. "How much is million dollars?"

"It's a lot, Zoey," Katherine's mom answered for her. "Swallow your food, please."

"Five million, actually," Katherine said. "A million apiece for the five strongest proposals for how the applicants would grow the wealth. They can't give it away; they must invest it somehow. Either in real estate or the stock market or in a business of some kind."

"And what did Wilson Devereaux, the millionaire, want with you?" Deidra asked.

"He offered me a job as program director, but I told him I'm happy at Bright Horizons. I love my job there."

"Wait," Deidre said, incredulously. "You turned down a program director job with a millionaire to stay an executive assistant? Probably just as well, that job is so far above your abilities right now. Maybe in five or ten years, you'd be ready for it."

"Your sister's right, Katherine," Mom said. "Better to keep the good job you're sure you can do than take a chance on a start-up. Besides, you have your hands full being a single mother with a young daughter to care for. Why add more complications to your life?"

Maybe they're right, Katherine thought. She didn't want to disappoint anyone, especially not Wilson Devereaux. Maybe she should go back to Bright Horizons and keep her life just the way it is. She had her daughter, the piece of Jake she was lucky enough to still have. Maybe that was enough.

CHAPTER 3

The next day, Katherine woke up thinking about the conversation at dinner the night before. And she thought about it all through breakfast and while she pruned the flowers in the backyard. The self-doubt she felt had after turning Wilson Devereaux's job offer turned to irritation. With her sister. Her parents. Most of all, with herself. Why did she always sell herself short? Why was she so afraid of failing?

She was so preoccupied with her thoughts, she didn't notice Zoey trying to get her attention.

"Mommy, can we go to the park?" Zoey tugged at Katherine's arm. "Please? Please take me to the park?" She bounced up and down excitedly.

"Okay, sweetie." Katherine stood up and brushed the garden soil off her pants. "But only for an hour or so." She kissed Zoey's forehead before they put together a picnic basket filled with muffins, fruit, and bagels, but no cream cheese because she knew that Zoey would lick it off the bagel and smear it all over her face and clothes, and get very little of it in her mouth.

It was a beautiful, sunny day and the park was full of children and parents. Katherine and Zoey found a lovely shady spot under a tree near the sandbox. The nearby flowers—planted in a rainbow pattern of reds, yellows, blues, and purple—gave off the most heavenly scents. The swings were empty, so Zoey had her favorite swing all to herself. As Katherine pushed her higher and higher on the swing, Zoey smiled brightly.

"This is the best day ever!" She shouted as she flew higher and higher into the sky. Katherine laughed at her daughter's enthusiasm.

"The park is pretty empty today," a woman said as she approached the swings with a little boy. "Looks like we have the place pretty much to ourselves."

"Yeah," Katherine said. "It's pretty nice, isn't it? And it's such a beautiful day."

"It is," the woman replied. "Hi, I'm Liz Lau. This is my son, Jackson."

"I'm Katherine. This is my daughter, Zoey."

"Do you like swinging really high?" Zoey asked Jackson.

"Yep," Jackson said. "I do!"

"Cool! Let's pretend we're flying when we go really high up," said Zoey.

"Well, I think the kids can handle the swings for a little while," Katherine said to Liz. "I have some coffee in a thermos over there if you'd like some"

"You read my mind," Liz said. "Lead on."

The two young mothers sat drinking coffee and watching their children run around having fun. The breeze rippled through the leaves of the tree above. Katherine closed her eyes and savored the feeling of the soft wind on her skin.

"Looks like the weight of the world is lifting off your shoulders," Liz said. "Bad week?"

"Depends on how you define a bad week," Katherine replied. "Let's just say I've had a weird week at work."

"Well, that sounds interesting. Weird is better than bad, isn't it?"

"I guess. How about you? I hope you're having a better work week than I am."

"I'm having a weird week at work, too. But I guess my problem is a good one to have," Liz said with a laugh.

"How do you mean?"

"Well, I'm lucky to run my own small business. I coach young mothers one-on-one on how to start a business while raising their families,"

"Wow," Katherine said, perking up with interest. She loved talking with small business owners. "That's impressive. Do you enjoy it?"

"I love helping people, but I can only help so many mothers one-on-one," Liz said. "I'm trying to find ways to grow my business, to pivot my business into a scalable model, where I can train other coaches in my approach and provide resources for them so they can coach other people."

"Sounds like you have a real vision for what you want to do with your coaching business."

"Oh, absolutely. By bringing additional coaches onboard, I can increase revenue while helping other people grow their businesses, too."

"How do you get clients?"

Liz thought about the question for a moment before replying. "Mostly word of mouth right now, but I'm looking for more venues to expand my reach. Redesigned my website. Hired a public relations person. But it's all so expensive. If I had the money, I could really sink it into my business, y'know?" Her eyes shone bright with passion, and Katherine could tell she really loved her business. "I won't give up though because, after all, what better way to grow your own business and wealth by helping other people grow their business, too?"

An idea sparked in Katherine's mind. Wilson Devereaux's how to grow your wealth program might be just the thing Liz needed. It would be a great way for her small businesses to grow and expand. In fact, her business would be perfect for it.

Katherine felt her heart flutter and she wasn't sure why. Maybe it was seeing Liz's passion for work and wanting some of that for herself. Perhaps it was a tiny seed of confidence growing in her chest, and the idea she could do this, whether

her family thought so or not. She was tired of listening to the negative voices that told her she could not achieve her goals. If Jake were still here, he would tell her not to listen to anyone else and just go for it.

She wanted to close her eyes and take a leap of faith. Now that she had made up her mind to do it, she really wanted to be Wilson Devereaux's program director. Could she do it? She'd never really had faith in herself before, this job could change her life. She even texted her family to tell them she was going to do it. Her parents' texts were reminders not to take too much of a risk. Deidre's text was a laughing face emoji.

"What if I told you that I knew a way to help get the money for you to grow your business?" Katherine asked.

Liz sat up on her knees, excited and eager to hear more. "I'd say I'm all ears."

"Then, give me your contact information," Katherine said, feeling excited and eager, too. "I have a phone call to make."

***

The next day, she made an appointment to see Wilson. When she arrived at his mansion, and was ushered to his office, she was nervous but excited, too. She was going to do this and make a success of it. "Remember, don't let your family tell you what you can and cannot do." she said to herself. Katherine just hoped the offer was still open.

Wilson walked into his office smiling. "Katherine! So glad you came to see me." he said, shaking her hand. "I think this is the start of a great partnership between us."

"I am so excited to take on this position, Wilson. I'm nervous, of course... but I'm ready to go." Katherine laughed nervously. "I want to help people change their lives."

Wilson sat down at his desk. "You said you have an applicant already lined up and we haven't even started. I'm impressed. So, tell me about Liz Lau."

"Well, I met Liz at the park. She was playing with her son, and from the moment I saw them together, I knew she loved being a mom. But what really impressed me about Liz was seeing how much she cared about making a difference in the world. She has this passion for her work, and I wanted to take that chance." Katherine smiled as she recounted the story of their meeting. "She's what you're looking for in any applicant, Wilson: passion for her work, drive, and determination."

"What *we* are looking for, Katherine," Wilson said. "You're my program director now. You've got this."

"What's the plan for getting more applicants?" Katherine asked.

Wilson grinned. "I was thinking you should do what you did with Ms. Lau. Go to everyday places and talk to everyday people," he said. "Start small and see where it takes you." He winked at Katherine.

"Well, that doesn't sound daunting at all," Katherine sighed. "Liz just opened up to me when we started talking about work."

"You'll be fine. Just talk to people and see if they're interested in what we're doing here. You can do this, Katherine." Wilson replied. "This program is going to change lives, and you'll be a part of that."

"There is one thing I've been thinking about. We need to consider applicants who not only have great proposals for how they would invest the money, but we should also consider applicants who want to help other people." Katherine explained. "People who want to help others will be more likely to really be invested in the program and its success."

"That's a great idea, Katherine. This will be the kind of thing we should definitely think about." Wilson asked.

"Absolutely," she replied. "This is an opportunity that only comes once in a lifetime. I will work with your assistant to get the proposal applications written up and forward it to Liz Lau with a note outlining the application process."

"Katherine, you sound different than you did the last time we met. You're really invested in this program." Wilson smiled and nodded his head. "I'm glad you agreed to be my program director. I'm so excited to see what you come up with next!"

"There's nothing more I want than to help people get into your millionaire investor program," Katherine replied. "To see people succeed and change their lives."

"I think you've found the new name for this program." Wilson scratched his chin and gave her a thoughtful look. "We should call it the Overnight Millionaire!"

"The Overnight Millionaire, huh?" Katherine repeated to herself. "I like it."

"It's nice to see you excited about this, Katherine," Wilson said as he stood up from his seat. "I have every confidence you'll find the right people for our program. Remember it's about quality not quantity. We want applicants who are going to make the most of this opportunity. So, don't rush it."

"Absolutely not," Katherine nodded her head as she stood up from her seat as well. "I'm going to take my time and really consider how we can turn this from a good program into a great one."

"Good. Don't forget, applicants have 30 days to submit their proposals for consideration," Wilson reminded her as he stood up. "And anyone who doesn't meet the deadline will not be considered for a financial reward."

Katherine nodded. "I understand completely," she replied. "Wish me luck!"

"Ah, you don't need luck, Katherine," Wilson smiled as he opened the office door for her. "You have skill and personality to fit this job. You're going to do just fine."

"Thanks, Wilson. I'll keep you updated," Katherine said as she headed out of the office.

Katherine's heart raced as she walked down the streets of her city. She had so much work to do and so little time to find the applicants she needed. The direction of the Overnight Millionaire program rested in her hands, and she was going to make a difference in a lot of people's lives.

CHAPTER FOUR

Katherine drove toward home; she had a few hours before she had to pick Zoey up at school. When she spotted her favorite coffee shop, she decided to stop for a celebratory cup of her usual caramel macchiato with extra caramel.

The Java Joint Café was a quirky little place with paintings of cats, burning candles at each table, stained-glass windows depicting flowers made from melted CDs, and a sign over the cash register that read "We Love You All the Time." When Katherine walked in, she was greeted by the smell of coffee and the gentle music of a piano instrumental soundtrack. As she waited in line, she thought about how she was going to find people who would be great applicants for the Overnight Millionaire program.

She ordered her drink, and a slice of banana bread, and sat in an overstuffed wing-backed chair at a table near the window. As she sipped her coffee, she listened to the baristas chat. It sounded like a young man named Sam—Katherine guessed he was in his mid 20s—had big dreams for his future. As he talked, Katherine listened intently even though she was trying not to appear obvious.

"You can never go wrong with real estate," Sam said to his co-worker as they cleaned the countertops. His black hair was cut short on the sides and the top was all curls. "My dad always says owning your own business is great because you get to be your own boss." Sam said. "I'm just trying to get him to see I'm ready to invest in my own buildings instead of just working as a property manager for him."

"Why are you working with your family, bro?" his colleague asked. He was tall and thin with dark hair combed to the side. He was wearing a red vest over his white shirt, and his name tag said 'Daniel'. "I couldn't work with my parents. You must be ready to get out in the world and do something different."

"I've learned a lot from my dad, he's a great teacher, but you're right, I need to find my own identity." Sam continued. "He's never approved of anything I wanted to do, even though it makes sense for me to be able to make investments on my own. If I can buy a few apartment buildings, the cash flow will be great, and the property values will increase over time. And I'll get all kinds of tax write-offs." Sam said with a smile.

Daniel shrugged as he wiped down another table. "I don't know, man, working with your dad during summer break from college was one thing. But is this really the way you want to spend your career?"

Sam's expression changed to something Katherine thought was either worry or contemplation. Or maybe it was the same sentiment she had about her own family. An 'I'll show them I can do this' attitude. She watched from her table as Sam went back to making drinks for the line of people waiting to be served.

After he had taken the order of the last person in line, Sam came over to Katherine's table. "Ma'am, is there anything else you'd like? We have more banana bread if you'd like."

She took another quick sip of her drink, then said "No thank you, but I couldn't help overhearing your conversation with Daniel over there. Sounds like you have big dreams."

Sam looked a little started at first. Was he worried what people hear when they come in here? Katherine wondered. "I didn't mean to eavesdrop," she said quickly. "But it sounded like you were talking about buying some buildings for investment purposes."

Sam smiled and relaxed a little bit. "Well, yes I am. I want my own business so badly I can taste it, and this is the next step for me." Sam held out his hand across the table and said with enthusiasm, "My name's Sam DeLeon, by the way."

"I'm Katherine Johnson."

"I see you in here a lot. You're one of our best customers." He said, pointing to the cup that bore his handwriting where he had documented her name. "I served your coffee today. Your name is on your cup."

"So, it does." She looked at her cup and laughed. Then she took a deep breath. She was nervous to ask but she thought if she could learn more about this young man's story, it will put her on a good path to finding the second person to apply for the program. "I am curious about where you see yourself going in the next few years. I may have a program you'd be interested in. When do you get off work?"

"Really?" Sam looked at her with interest and he nodded. He said quickly, "I'd love to talk if you can wait for a bit. I'll be through here in about 15 minutes."

Katherine checked her phone. She still had several hours before she had to pick up Zoey. "I have time. We can chat right here when you're through if that's ok with you."

"Sounds great. I'll be over as soon as I clock out."

Katherine checked her phone and drank her coffee as she waited. She was almost finished with her drink when Sam came back to the table. She cleared some emails, checked her schedule, and replied to Mr. Devereaux about the website he asked his tech guys to develop. It wouldn't be ready until the next day, but at least she had an email address where applicants could submit their proposals.

Sam excused himself from the barista bar to go to the back office, presumably to clock out. A few minutes later, emerged and brought two more cups of coffee with him. "Sorry I kept you waiting," he said as he handed her one of the cups and sat down across from her. "I really appreciate you talking to me about whatever this opportunity is. You really have my curiosity piqued."

"Good," she replied. "I'm interested in learning more about you and your plans for the future. Your ambitions. Your dreams. Any plans you have for your goals. I did hear you saying certain things about your dad, real estate investment opportunities, and business-related tax deductions. You seem like a very astute young man. This program could be perfect for someone like you." She pulled a small pad of post-it notes out of her purse and wrote her name and number down on it, as well as the email address for submitting the proposals. "Sorry," she said. "I'm so new in my role that I don't have business cards yet." She handed it to Sam with its corners between her fingers so he could read.

"Overnight Millionaire Program?" he asked with a curious lift of an eyebrow.

"Mr. Wilson Devereaux is looking for five people for this new program."

"Devereaux? The real estate magnate?"

"That's the one. But you would know all about him since your dad is in real estate," she said. "Mr. Devereaux wants to help people learn how to grow their wealth. So, the program is open to anyone. Applicants will submit a proposal to describe how they would invest one million dollars."

"One million?" His eyes widened, and he sat up straight in the chair. Then his eyes narrowed. "What's the catch?"

"Not exactly a 'catch', per se, but there are requirements. First, you can't give the money away to charity, you must invest it somehow. And you need to lay out how your business or project will help other people, too."

"Ok. What else?" he asked, clearly interested in finding out more.

"Proposals must be submitted in the next 30 days. Even if someone has a great idea, and we'd love to fund an investment with the one-million-dollar seed money, but if the application is late, it won't be considered."

"That sounds fair enough," he said.

"I know, but owning my own business is what's going to make me stand out. My dad has been involved in real estate for thirty years; he always tells me that people will learn more from doing than they would learn from reading about it forever." Sam said. "He wants me to wait until I'm thirty to invest. He doesn't think I have the experience yet."

Katherine thought for a second, then said, "Tell me why you think you're ready to invest now instead of having to wait like your dad asks?"

Sam took a deep breath and rubbed his hands together. "I know it's true that investing in real estate is the smartest option when you're young because it provides positive cash flow, equity growth, and flexibility when you can use depreciation for tax write-offs. I'm ready to take on the responsibility of owning an apartment building. I'll start small, first." He reached for his phone and opened a file stored on his cloud server. "I've been working with a mentor and learning a lot about multifamily investing. I've already written a business plan," Sam said, opening a file of different resources and blueprints from nearby apartment complexes he was researching.

"Wow," Katherine said. "You're really getting prepared. So, are you interested?"

"I'll admit, this sounds a little bit out there, but I'm so tired of working here and for my dad, trying to prove myself. If I could invest in an apartment building, I could really get my career off the ground. It's hard for me to afford things like a car or even my own apartment." He looked down at the note with the contact information on it. "And if you can help me do something with this... Well, shoot. I have nothing to lose by applying right?"

"That's exactly what Mr. Devereaux thought when he came up with this idea. We're looking for people who are passionate about their careers and want to make their dreams a reality. This is for someone who wants to increase their wealth—the only limits are your imagination, commitment, and drive to succeed." She placed her cup on the table as she stood up. "I know it seems like a long way away for both of us, really. If you're interested in learning more, the website will be up tomorrow, and you can download the application from there. Then, submit it by email to the address on the note there." She paused a minute. "So, what do you think?"

"I'm definitely interested! Thank you so much, Katherine." Sam reached across the table and shook her hand firmly.

Katherine smiled back at him. "Awesome. Ok, so get on the website tomorrow. If you have any trouble accessing it, then send me an email. I've put my address on that paper, too."

"I can't tell you what this means to me," Sam said, his voice choked with emotion. He looked at her, incredulous for a moment, taking in what she had just told him. He gave her another huge smile, then jumped out of his chair and gave her a big hug.

She hugged him back and, had to admit, it felt amazing to be on the ground floor of watching other people's dreams come true. "Good. We'll look forward to your proposal, then."

Sam nodded. "Yes, thank you again."

Katherine got up from the table and turned quickly to leave before she became too emotional herself. She'd never had the opportunity to make this kind of difference in someone's life before. Once outside on the pavement, she turned to look back through the window into the coffee shop. Sam looked like he was describing their conversation to his co-worker with animated gestures, and then began pumping his fists in the air.

It was good to see him so excited about the program, and Katherine walked to her car with a spring in her step and a smile on her face. Maybe she really could do this job.

CHAPTER 5

The next morning, after Katherine dropped Zoey off at school, she poured herself another cup of coffee and fired up her laptop. She checked her email and saw a message from Wilson Devereaux about Sam DeLeon's application for the Overnight Millionaire Program.

"Awesome," she said to herself. "I'm so happy Sam filled out his application. I knew Wilson would be excited about him." She opened the email and read it.

Hi Katherine,

I'm very excited about Mr. DeLeon's application. I think he is a great fit for the Overnight Millionaire Program. You're doing a great job finding applicants. Keep up the good work!

Wilson

After sending a reply email back to Wilson, Katherine browsed the internet, looking for inspiration for who might be the next program applicant. She read several articles before she ran across one about a new business open in town.

Sweet Soul Creations is a new local bakery and café owned and operated by Paris-trained pastry chef Billie Palmer. Offering a wide variety of deliciously decorated cakes, cupcakes, and cookies, Sweet Soul Creations also offers high-quality Sweet Table catering that is perfect for special occasions such as weddings, baby showers, and birthday parties.

When asked about her business, Billie says, "I don't know if there's a better place in the world to be right now. It's been a long road to get my baby off the ground, and a lot of hard work, but I'm finally living my dream. My business is small, and we're just starting out but I'm going to give it my best shot. I have amazing employees who are just as passionate about baking as I am. It's all good."

"This looks promising," Katherine said. And the more she read, the more she thought Billie Palmer would be an amazing candidate for the Overnight Millionaire program. She read her bio and, then checked out Sweet Soul Creations' website.

The pictures of Billie's product looked delicious and gorgeous, with a mix of traditional pastries and special creations with exotic flavors in various shapes and sizes. Katherine browsed Billie's website and Facebook page, finding out more about the woman that excited her.

As she read through her About section on the website, she came across a business magazine article link that listed Billie as one of several Black, female up-and-coming entrepreneurs to watch. She clicked the link. The article was an effusive piece about an apprenticeship program Billie ran in her business.

Billie Palmer's 'Sweet Soul Beginnings' is a paid apprenticeship program that provides a unique opportunity for young people who are passionate about baking to learn from Paris-trained pastry chef Billie Palmer. The apprenticeship program will prepare young people for work in the culinary field with hands-on experience, guidance, and support to help them launch their own careers. It is open to young people between the ages of 18 and 25.

"Bingo," Katherine said, excitedly. A young entrepreneur with a fledgling business who was already helping others to get a leg up in the world could be the next person to get an opportunity of a lifetime.

***

As she drove to the school pick up zone to collect Zoey, Katherine couldn't stop thinking about Billie Palmer and her bakery. After a brief chat with Zoey's teacher, she bundled her little girl into the car.

"I don't know about you, but I am in the mood for cupcakes," she told Zoey as she fastened her safety belt. "What do you think? Shall we go find some?"

Zoey thought for a second and frowned. "You said we could have cupcakes on Friday if I do a good job at school this week. But it's not Friday yet."

"I know it's only Thursday, but I read about this cool bakery earlier, and I think we should go today. What do you think?"

"Okay," Zoey finally said, "but I get to pick what cupcake I want."

Katherine laughed as she buckled herself into the driver's seat. Six-year-olds are never hard to convince when cupcakes are involved. She pulled the car onto the road leading to the village square, and in less than 15 minutes, they arrived at the bakery.

Sweet Soul Creations was in a charming building that boasted two large picture windows showcasing all the sweet treats on offer. Inside, the smell of chocolate and fruit and fresh baked goods filled the air. One wall was staged with tiers of artfully arranged cupcakes, while another showcased cakes decorated with intricate figures, flowers, and abstract designs. The shop was decorated simply but elegantly - clean lines, cream-colored walls, and wooden furniture that matched the hardwood floors perfectly. A tall counter stood at one end of the room where customers could place their orders or watch as items were prepared.

Two petite women worked behind the counter, both wearing white lab coats adorned with Sweet Soul name tags over casual clothes - one had dark braids pulled back into a bun at her neck; the other wore her pale pink hair piled in a messy bun atop her head. A plump, cheerful woman with curly hair greeted Katherine and Zoey as they browsed through the display cases.

"Welcome to Sweet Soul Creations," she said. "Take your time looking around. We have so many tasty treats, it will be hard to make up your mind."

"I believe you," Katherine replied, cheerfully. "Everything looks wonderful," she paused.

"Excuse me, but you're Billie Palmer, aren't you?"

"That's me! Is there something I can help you with?"

"I'm Katherine Johnson," she said, then gestured to her daughter. "This is Zoey, my six-year-old. I read some of the interviews about your opening. How long have you been open?"

"Oh, we've been open for a couple of months now. It's been a wild ride but incredibly rewarding."

Katherine smiled and shook her hand. "You have a lovely shop. Do you mind if I ask more about this apprenticeship program you offer?"

Billie beamed at Katherine and motioned to the counter where Zoey was standing, looking at the cupcakes on display in one of the cases. "Of course. But it looks like your little girl is having trouble choosing a cupcake. How about I make you a deal? Let's help Miss Zoey to choose her favorite flavor, then we can chat about the apprenticeship program."

"Sounds like a plan," Katherine said. They joined the little girl at the largest display case filled with rows and rows of cupcakes. "Zoey, what kind of cupcake do you want? Chocolate? Vanilla?"

Zoey looked up at Katherine, then pointed to a deep pink cupcake frosted with sunny yellow icing and garnished with strawberry hearts and lemon-shaped candies. "That one!" she said happily. "Is it ok, Mommy?"

"Sure is, honey," Katherine said. "What flavor is that?"

"That is our Strawberry Lemonade Dream cupcake," Billie said with a smile. "It's one of our best sellers."

"Looks amazing to me," Katherine said. ""Everything looks fantastic. I don't know how I will choose." She cast an admiring glance at the rich variety of cupcakes and desserts on display—chocolate tortes and mousses, red velvet cheesecakes and dark chocolate cupcakes with ganache icing between layers of cake.

Billie gave her an appraising look. "As far as cupcake flavors go, I'm pretty good at guessing someone's favorite. You look like a chocolate kind of girl to me."

"You're right," Katherine said with a smile. "I am. I love chocolate in all its forms."

"Sometimes," Zoey cut in, "Mommy eats chocolate for breakfast when she thinks I'm not looking."

Billie chuckled. "I like your Mommy," she said to Zoey.

She turned back to Katherine with a warm smile. "Well, I think you'll love our Chocolate Salted Caramel Cupcake."

"Then, I will take your advice," Katherine said as she pulled up her cash app on her phone and paid for the treats.

Cupcakes in hand, Katherine and Zoey sat at one of the wood tables near the big picture windows. The traffic in the shop picked up and soon, there was a small crowd of customers peering into the display cases. Billie helped the girls behind the counter with the customers and Katherine watched the interactions, taking mental notes on the high-quality service and personal touch each staff membered gave to each person as if they were the only customer in the bakery.

As Zoey ate her cupcake, Katherine watched the customers coming in and out. They were all treated with the utmost respect, patience, and friendliness. Billie herself was busy with her work but always made sure to greet each customer coming in, asking about how they were doing or if there was anything she could help them with. She also helped others pick out treats, suggesting flavors of cupcakes or cakes that might satisfy their cravings for desserts.

"She's so nice," Katherine said wistfully when she saw Billie showing a middle-aged woman who had just moved into town some of the most popular items on the menu.

Zoey nodded while licking off her lemon icing. "Yeah! She reminds me of my teacher, Mrs. McCurdy."

Katherine chuckled at Zoey's comparison to one of her schoolteachers. "How is she like Mrs. McCurdy?"

"Because she's nice!" Zoey said. "And pretty. And she helps people." She paused to take a sip of her milk. "She makes really good cupcakes, too."

Katherine laughed again. "Yes, she does."

A few minutes later, Billie joined them at their table. She sat down and took a sip of her own drink. "Having fun?"

"Yes," Zoey said happily. She finished off her cupcake and brushed away some crumbs from the side of her face. "I like it here."

Billie smiled then turned to Katherine. "So, you want to hear about our apprenticeship program. What would you like to know?"

"I'd like to know how you got the idea to start an apprentice program at the same time you launched your business," Katherine said. "Some people would say that's a bit crazy. Why not launch the business first and then launch the apprenticeship later."

Billie settled into her seat, a thoughtful expression on her face. "It started when I studied at Le Cordon Bleu in Paris. I wanted to specialize in patisseries and chocolates, but I didn't have the money to pay for classes." She shrugged. "After a lot of persistence and some lucky breaks, I got one of their scholarships."

"Is that where you got the idea for your apprenticeship program?"

"Yes. Before I went to Paris, I ran a small cupcake business out of my home. It was going okay but not great and mostly just brought in enough money for me to pay the bills." She paused briefly. "When I got back from Paris, I wanted to do more than just run a little cupcake business. I wanted to build a business model where I could fill people's need for purpose as well as filling their tummies with desserts. But..." her voice trailed off.

"But what?" Katherine asked, concerned.

"It's a struggle to run the business and the apprenticeship program at the same time. Most small businesses don't turn profits in their first year, and I'm far from it at the moment. I would love, someday, to expand the bakery and cafe apprenticeship program beyond the two people I have right now." she paused. "You asked why I didn't wait to start the apprentice program and the simple fact is that there are other people out there who need a helping hand—young people with very few skills and need a bit of a leg up in the world."

"So," Katherine smiled wide and leaned her elbows on the table. "What would you do if you had one million dollars at your disposal?"

"A million?" Her eyes went wide, and she blew out a rush of air in the exciting prospect of such a sum of money. "I would expand my business. Maybe franchise it. And I would help those new business owners start their own apprentice programs. I believe that you can achieve your own goals by helping others achieve theirs."

"Well, then, Billie Palmer," Katherine said, her eyes gleaming. "Have I got an opportunity for you."

CHAPTER 6

All morning long, Katherine replayed the conversation with Billie Palmer in her head. It had been a great conversation, and she felt so lucky to be able to help the young entrepreneur apply for Wilson's program. She was so engrossed in her work thoughts, she let her coffee go cold in her cup twice. Something she rarely ever did.

It took Zoey tugging on Katherine's sleeve to realize her daughter was speaking to her. "Mommy, are we still going to the bookstore today?" The girl asked. "You said we could go on Saturday, and it's Saturday now so can we go?"

Katherine pulled her thoughts away from work and back to the present. She kept thinking about the great meeting with Billie Palmer, and how much progress she had made, so far, with finding candidates for Wilson's new program. She loved her executive assistant job at Bright Horizons, but now she'd had a taste of working directly with people to help change their lives, she wanted to do more. Wilson's offer was a great opportunity to help people in a much bigger way than she ever could through her day job.

"Sure," Katherine said with a smile. "Let's get some breakfast first, and then we'll go."

Katherine made blueberry pancakes for Zoey, and they talked about the books Zoey wanted to read and the games she wanted to play. After they finished breakfast, they went to Stories and Scribbles, the independent bookstore down the street from their apartment. Zoey skipped to the children's section and pulled out a few books while Katherine browsed the business section.

The store was under new management; the new owners were a young couple, and they were in the process of renovating the store. Katherine had just picked up a book on business start-ups when a young woman caught her attention. She was dressed in a simple skirt and blouse and wore a name tag that said "Ellie". She was shelving books, and Katherine guessed she was either an employee or one of the new owners of the store.

The woman noticed Katherine glancing over at her several times as she picked through a few books and said, "Hi. Can I help you find something?"

"Maybe," Katherine said, picking up the business start-up book she had just been looking at. "I'm looking for books about how people grow their wealth. What do you think of this one?"

"It's a good book," Ellie said. "There are so many books about getting rich, and everyone has different ideas about what it takes. But I think the most important thing is to find something you're passionate about, and then figure out how to make money doing it." She paused a moment to look around the store with a satisfied smile. "I think that's what we're trying to do here. We want to help people find books they love, and that's kind of our passion. My husband's and mine, I mean."

"You're the new owners," Katherine smiled.

"Yes, we are," Ellie said. "We just took over a few weeks ago."

"That's really exciting," Katherine said, grinning wide. "This is a great bookstore. My daughter, Zoey, and I love it here. We come every Saturday."

"Thank you," Ellie said. "We're trying to make it a place where people can come and find something they love, whether it's a book, or a gift, or just a quiet place to read. It has always been our dream to own a bookstore, and it takes a lot of passion and dedication to make it work because we put in some long hours here. You've got to really love it, you know?"

Great work ethic? Check. Passion for her work? Check. Loves to help others get what they want? Check. Ellie ticked all the boxes for what Wilson was looking for in candidates. And, from the sounds of it, her husband had the same drive and dedication that she did. Katherine was certain the couple could do great things with the one-million-dollar funding opportunity if they applied for Wilson's program.

Katherine felt the adrenaline start to pump as she imagined what the couple could do with the money. They could expand the store and hire more employees. They could invest in the property, maybe even buy it outright instead of leasing it and make it even more beautiful than it was now. They could expand their selection of books and offer a wider variety of gifts. The possibilities were endless, and Katherine couldn't wait to tell Ellie about them.

"You know, I think you would be great for a new program that Wilson Devereaux is developing," Katherine said, smiling at Ellie. "He's looking for people with a great work ethic and a passion for helping others get what they want."

"Wilson Devereaux?" Ellie asked, her eyebrows furrowing in concentration. "The big millionaire guy who's always in the local newspaper?"

"That's the one. I'm helping him develop a program that will award $1 million to people who have great plans for how they would invest the money and learn to grow their wealth," Katherine explained. "You can do anything with the money you like except give it away to charity. You can invest it or use it to start—or improve—a business, or anything you want. It's really a great opportunity."

"What happens if you don't win the one million dollars?"

"Even if you're not awarded the one million, you will still get $100,000 just for applying. I mean, you really can't go wrong. At the end of the day, you'd still wind up with a sizable amount of money."

"I don't know," Ellie said, her face still furrowed in concern. "It sounds too good to be true."

"It's not," Katherine said, nodding earnestly. "Wilson is a really great guy. He's doing this because he wants to help people achieve their dreams and learn the importance of growing their wealth. I think you should apply. You could really do some amazing things with the money."

"So, this millionaire wants to help people grow their wealth." Ellie's expression was a mix of disbelief and uncertainty. She was clearly intrigued by the offer, but Katherine could tell she was still hesitant. "Why would he do that?"

"I know it sounds too good to be true," Katherine said. "But I promise you, it's real. I even left a job I love because I believe in this program so much. We have several people who are applying, already, and I think you would be perfect for it."

"Well, I don't know," Ellie said, biting her lip. "It sounds like a lot of work. Would we have to show our wealth actually increased if we took the money? And what if our wealth didn't increase and we lost money? There's no guarantee that what we might do with it would increase our wealth. If we invested in our business and something went wrong, we could lose all that money we were given."

"There's always that risk, sure, and it is a lot of work," Katherine admitted. "But it's worth it. And I'm here to help you every step of the way if you're interested in applying. Why don't you talk it over with your husband and see what he thinks? I'll give you my number and we can touch base in a couple of days. Zoey and I live right up the street."

Ellie took the piece of paper with Katherine's number on it and tucked it into her pocket. "I'll talk to my husband and see what he thinks," she said.

"If you're interested, I can give you more information. Wilson is looking for people who have great ideas and are passionate about making them happen."

"I don't know," Ellie said, shaking her head. "My husband and I are just starting out in business, and we just leased this place. I'm not sure if we're ready for something like that."

Katherine could see the doubt in Ellie's eyes and knew anyone who needed convincing to apply would likely not be a good candidate for the program. "That's okay," Katherine said, patting Ellie on the arm. "You can think about it and let me know if you're interested. No pressure."

"Thank you," Ellie said, giving Katherine a small smile. "We just have so much going on here, with the store and our kids. I'm not sure if we can take on anything else right now." She paused; her eyes narrowed in skepticism. "Besides, there has to be a catch. There's always a catch."

"I understand," Katherine said. "Like I said, no pressure. You've got my number, and the website is there, too. Take a look, then you and I can catch up later this week."

Katherine turned away from Ellie and started browsing the kids' section shelves, looking for a book for Zoey. As she scanned the titles, she couldn't help but think about what Ellie had said. It was true that the couple had a lot going on, but Katherine still thought they would be great candidates for the program. She knew from experience that it was often when people were the busiest that they needed extra support to reach their goals. But they must see the value, and the importance, for themselves.

Katherine spent the next forty-five minutes looking through books with Zoey. She also watched Ellie out of the corner of her eye and noticed how easily she interacted with her customers; she was charming and personable, and it was clear that she loved her work. After Zoey had picked out a few books, they made their way to the checkout counter. As she paid for her purchase, Katherine could see the wheels in her head turning. She was clearly intrigued by what Katherine said, despite her earlier hesitation.

"I'm glad you found some books you like, Zoey," Ellie said as she packed the books into a cloth shopping bag.

"I did," Zoey said, beaming up at her. "These books look really fun. I'm going to take them to school this week for show and tell."

"I'm sure your teacher will love that," Ellie said. "And I'm glad you had fun today." She turned to Katherine. "I will talk to my husband and see what he thinks about the program."

"That's all I can ask. And if there are any questions I can answer, you have my number."

***

Katherine spent the next few days thinking about Ellie and her husband and how they could potentially benefit from the Overnight Millionaire program. She knew that Ellie was hesitant, but she also thought there was a good chance the couple would be interested once they learned more about it. On Wednesday evening, Katherine called Ellie and asked if she wanted to come over for dinner so they could chat about the program in more detail.

"I don't think so," Ellie said. "My husband is even more skeptical about the whole deal than I am. He doesn't want to waste our time with something that's not going to pan out."

"I understand," Katherine said. "But I think it would be worth your while to at least hear the rest of the story. I could arrange a meeting with Wilson Devereaux if you're still skeptical."

"No, thanks," Ellie's sigh was a little heavier, bordering on impatience. "Thank you for sharing the information with us. But we're going to pass."

Katherine hung up the phone and frowned. Why wouldn't they at least listen to what she had to say? She was sure they would change their mind if they could just see what she did. But she also knew that it wasn't her place to push them any further. Ellie and her husband had made their decision, and Katherine respected that.

The next few days were filled with so many "no" answers, Katherine lost count. She had spoken to at least ten other people who seemed to be great program candidates, but no one seemed interested. And many of them thought it was simply a scam because it seemed too good to be true.

Sometimes, people don't want to believe that something so great could exist for them. Katherine had been in their shoes before, and she knew how they felt. But she also knew that the program was real, and it could change their lives if they only gave it a chance.

Katherine's phone buzzed, it was a text message from her sister, Deirdre.

So, how's your little money-making scheme going?

Great, Katherine thought, *just great*. Her sister seemed to have a radar that told her when Katherine was feeling her lowest, and she chose that point to twist the screws. Katherine sighed and knew that if she didn't answer, Deirdre would just keep texting her.

It's not a money-making scheme. Katherine typed back. *It's a program that will change people's lives.*

Katherine took a deep breath. Hoping that somehow, her Grinch of a sister might grow a heart. Unfortunately, the hope didn't last long.

You're such a sucker, Katherine. You always have been. You're going to be disappointed when this whole thing falls through.

Katherine felt her temper flare. She knew that her sister was only trying to get under her skin, but it still hurt. Why couldn't Deirdre be happy for her? Why couldn't she be supportive?

I'm not a sucker and this isn't going to fall through.

Don't you have better things to do than text me?

"Mommy? Are you ok?" Zoey asked as she climbed up into Katherine's lap for cuddles.

"I'm just tired, sweetie."

Truthfully, she was more than tired. She was exhausted – from the long days of trying to drum up interest in the Overnight Millionaire program, and from the never-ending texts from her sister Deirdre.

Katherine buried her nose in her daughter's sweet-smelling hair and inhaled. Even though everything else in her life felt like it was crumbling, Zoey was still the one thing that was always solid. "I'm fine, baby. I'm just a little frustrated right now. But I'll get through it. I always do."

"Is it Auntie Deirdre again?" Zoey asked. "She's cranky."

Katherine nodded and smiled at her daughter's description of Deirdre as just being 'cranky', like a nap was all that would be needed to put her world right and bring out the rainbows and sunshine of her personality. "She is a bit cranky, isn't she?"

"My teacher says that when someone is always so mean to you, it's because they're not very happy people," Zoey said.

Katherine was a bit surprised by her daughter's wisdom. "Your teacher is a very smart lady."

"I know," Zoey said with a nod. "She says I'm smart too."

"And she's right," Katherine said. "You are the smartest six-year-old that I know."

Zoey giggled and snuggled closer to Katherine. "I love you, Mommy."

"I love you too, sweetheart," Katherine said.

Even though she was feeling low, Katherine knew that she couldn't stay in that place for long. She had to keep moving forward and fighting for what she believed in. And she had to do it for herself and for her daughter. Because they were worth it.

Katherine kissed Zoey on the forehead and hugged her close. Family was supposed to be the people who loved you and supported you, no matter what. But sometimes, it felt like family were the people who loved to watch you fail.

She took some deep breaths. She just needed two more people to say 'yes'. Maybe she was looking in the wrong places. Maybe she was looking for the wrong people. She stared at her sister's text messages and realized things that Deirdre had in common with the people who were skeptical about the funding program: Doubt.

None of them could believe what they couldn't see or touch. They all thought that something this good couldn't be real, and so they were looking for ways to prove that it wasn't. In Deirdre's case, perhaps she was so used to feeling superior to Katherine that she couldn't bear the thought of her sister being successful at something. Or maybe she was just afraid that Katherine would finally be able to outshine her.

Katherine put her phone down and thought about what she could do differently. She needed people who were willing to take a chance, even if they weren't sure it would work out in the end. She needed people like Ellie and her husband- people who were skeptics, but still open-minded enough to listen. And then she had an idea.

Katherine put her phone down and went to bed, determined to try again the next day. She was going to find two more people who were willing to give the program a chance, no matter what it took. And she was going to try to not worry about the people who couldn't see the forest for the trees.

CHAPTER 7

The morning alarm rang on Katherine's phone and being a chronic snooze button addict, she hit the button for the sixth time before finally dragging herself out of bed. Thank goodness the school district had a teacher's in-service day scheduled and Zoey didn't have to go to school. She glanced at the time, and it was well past nine. She was already kicking herself for not being more proactive in getting up. It was already the middle of the month, and she only had a few weeks left to submit proposals.

Her inner critic was already working overtime and, no big surprise, the voice sounded exactly like her sister. *You're going to fail. You don't know what you're doing. Mr. Devereaux is going to see exactly how worthless you are.* It was a litany of negative self-talk garbage that Katherine let run in her head for longer than she should have. Katherine tried to ignore the voice and focus on what she needed to do that day. She grabbed her phone and began going through her emails while having breakfast.

As she sipped her coffee, the phone buzzed and Wilson Devereaux's number flash across her screen. She sighed, steeled herself for the conversation, and answered the phone.

"Good morning, Katherine," Wilson Devereaux said, brightly. "I just wanted to check in and see how you're doing."

"Me? Oh, I'm...I'm fine," Katherine lied. She had barely looked at the three applications from Liz, Sam, and Billie.

"I have to say, I'm impressed with the caliber of applicants you've found so far."

"Really?" Katherine asked, trying not to sound more relieved than excited. Three applicants meant that Liz, Sam, and Billie all followed through on submitting their applications. "That's good news."

"Good? It's fantastic!" Wilson gushed. "I'm looking forward to seeing who else you bring to the table. I have a feeling this program is going to be a smashing success."

Katherine was doing her best to keep a brave face for Wilson, but inside she was fighting a massive battle with the critical voices in her head. She could feel the doubts and worries creeping in, telling her that she wasn't good enough and that she would never be able to find two more people to apply for the program.

She tried to shut out the voices, but they were getting louder and more persistent with each passing minute. She could picture Wilson's face, beaming with pride at her success, and she didn't want to let him down. The doubts kept creeping in, telling her that she was making a mistake. That there was no way this program would work. That she was only kidding herself if she thought she could find more people to submit proposals.

Katherine took a deep breath and tried to focus on the conversation with Wilson. "Yeah, it is. We're gonna knock it out of the park," she said, doing her best to sound upbeat. "I'm headed out in a little while and I'm sure we'll have even more applicants in the pipeline soon."

There was a pause on the other end of the line. And when Wilson finally spoke, it sounded like he was choosing his words carefully. "Hey, kiddo, are you sure you're okay?" he asked. "You sound a little...off."

Katherine's heart sunk at the question. She knew she couldn't keep up the act for much longer. "No, no, I'm fine," she lied again. "Just a little tired this morning."

"Okay," he said slowly, obviously not believing her but deciding not to push it. "I know entrepreneurship can be really stressful. I want you to know that I'm thrilled with the progress you've made so far. But if you're feeling overwhelmed, or like you can't find more applicants, then just tell me. I'm not going to be upset with you. I just want what's best for the program."

Katherine was silent for a minute, trying to process his words. It was such a relief to hear him say that he wasn't expecting her to find even more candidates like the first three, but she still had to find two more people.

"I'll find more applicants, Mr. Devereaux," Katherine said, finally finding her voice. "I promise."

Wilson's voice was warm and encouraging when he spoke again. "I have no doubt about that, Katherine. You're a fighter. I can tell that you're going to make this program work no matter what. Just remember, this is just the first go-around for the program. We have plenty of time to make it a success."

Katherine was silent for a minute, trying to take in Wilson's words. He was right, of course. There was no need to stress out about the program. She could do this.

"Thank you, Mr. Devereaux," Katherine said finally. "I appreciate your confidence in me."

"You're welcome, kiddo," Mr. Devereaux said. "And Katherine?"

"Yeah?"

"We are friends, now. Don't forget to call me Wilson."

"Thank you, Wilson," Katherine said, her voice trembling a little bit. "I really appreciate your support."

He chuckled softly. "You don't have to thank me, kiddo. I'm just happy to see you succeed."

Katherine's eyes filled with tears at the words, and she had to fight to keep from breaking down on the phone. She was so grateful for Wilson's support. He was the only one who believed in her enough to give her this chance. Somehow, she needed to believe in herself as much as he did.

"I'll talk to you soon, okay?" Wilson asked.

"Yep. Talk to you soon and, Wilson?" she added.

"Yeah?"

"Thank you for believing in me."

Katherine hung up the phone and collapsed onto her bed, the tears finally spilling over. She allowed herself to cry for a few minutes, letting out all the fear and doubt that had been swirling around in her head. Then she took a deep breath, wiped her tears away, and stood up. It was time to get to work. She had a promise to keep, and she wasn't going to let Wilson—or herself—down.

Katherine decided it was time for a little self-care, something that would lift her spirits and get her motivated. She asked Belinda—her neighbor who frequently watched Zoey—if she could watch her daughter for a few hours so she could get some things done. Belinda was happy to help, and Katherine was soon pulling on her running shoes and hitting the pavement.

The fresh air and exercise did wonders for Katherine's mood, and she took the time to really focus on her breathing and her surroundings. She noticed the way the sun felt on her skin and the way the breeze cooled her as she ran. She paid attention to the way her body felt as she moved and pushed herself to go a little bit further than she had the day before.

By the time she made it back to her place, Katherine felt like a new person. She was refreshed, relaxed, and ready to take on whatever came her way. She showered and changed into some comfortable clothes before sitting down at her kitchen table to make a list of things she needed to do.

First on the list was finding candidates for Wilson's program. She knew it wouldn't be easy, but she was determined to succeed and not let the inner voices bully her the way they had earlier in the day. Katherine made a few phone calls and sent out some emails, reaching out to people she thought might be interested in the opportunity.

She noticed one particular name on her list, a woman named Sarah Mills who had been through a lot of tough times in her life, and she knew that if anyone could benefit from this program, it was her.

Katherine decided to call Sarah, so she picked up the phone and dialed her number. Sarah picked up on the second ring, and Katherine took a deep breath before diving in.

"Hi, Sarah. It's Katherine Johnson. Long time, no talk to."

"Katherine! Yeah, I guess it has been a while. How are you? How's that sweet girl of yours?"

"I'm good, and Zoey is growing like a weed. It's like every time I blink, she grows another inch."

"That's the truth. Benjamin is thirteen going on thirty and towers over me now. Not only that, he thinks he knows everything, and I'm pretty sure he's trying to make me earn every single one of my gray hairs."

Katherine and Sarah laughed, and they chatted for a few minutes before Katherine brought up the reason for her call.

"I'm actually calling about something kind of important," Katherine said. "Do you know Wilson Devereaux?"

She paused a moment. "The big real estate tycoon guy? That Wilson Devereaux? He's everywhere and kinda hard to ignore."

"Yeah, he's definitely that. Anyway, he's started this new business funding program called the Overnight Millionaire, and he asked me to find candidates for it."

Katherine went on to explain the program and what it entailed. From the way she was making agreement noises, she could tell Sarah was thinking it over, but she was also hesitant.

"Are you serious?" Sarah's voice was incredulous. "This sounds too good to be true," she said skeptically. "Why me? There must be other people more qualified than me."

"I don't know about that," Katherine said. She knew that Sarah underestimated her own skills, but she had seen her move mountains when she put her mind to it. "You're one of the most resilient people I know, Sarah. You're smart and resourceful. I think you could really benefit from this program, and I think Wilson would just love you."

"I don't know what to say," Sarah said, sounding overwhelmed.

"Just say yes," Katherine said, knowing her voice was a little too eager. "I promise you won't regret it."

Sarah was quiet for a moment, and Katherine could hear the gears in her head-turning. Finally, she spoke.

"I don't know. I'd have to see more about the program and talk to my husband before I make a decision. I'm not the kind of person who just leaps in and builds castles in the air."

Katherine had expected this response, and she was ready for it. "I understand that Sarah. I'm not either. But I can promise you that this is a legitimate opportunity and Wilson is a good guy. He's been helping people for years now and he's never let anyone down. This is a once-in-a-lifetime opportunity, and I really think you should at least consider it. I can send you more information about the program, and if you have any questions, don't hesitate to call or email me."

"I understand," Katherine felt a bit dejected. She had psyched herself up for the phone call and now she felt like she had come up short. "Thank you for considering it, Sarah."

"No problem," Sarah said. "I'll talk to you soon."

They said their goodbyes and hung up, and Katherine leaned back in her chair with a sigh, feeling a little deflated and discouraged. She had been so sure that Sarah would be on board, but now it sounded like she wasn't really interested at all. Maybe it was a mistake to do this presentation over the phone.

Katherine sat down at her computer and started drafting an email to send to Sarah with more information about the program. She was just about to hit send when her phone rang. She glanced at the caller ID and saw that it was Sarah.

"Sarah! Hey, what's up?"

"Hey, girl," Sarah said. "Are you busy?"

Katherine felt a surge of hopeful expectation wash over her. She crossed her fingers in hopes that Sarah had been thinking things over and maybe she was more interested in the program than she let on.

"I was just typing out the program details to send to you," Katherine said. "What's up?

Sarah hesitated for a moment before she spoke. "I talked to my husband about your program and we're going to take a pass on this one."

"Oh, okay," Katherine said, trying not to sound disappointed. She had really hoped Sarah would say yes. "Can I ask why?"

"It's just...not something we can do right now."

Right now. Well, that was something. Maybe the door has not completely slammed in my face. "I know it sounds too good to be true, but Wilson Devereaux is a stand-up guy, and—."

"It's not just that," Sarah said quickly. "We just don't think it's the right time for us. We're really busy with the kids and our business and we just don't have time to take on another project."

Yep. It was definitely a bad idea to talk with Sarah over the phone. Should have talked to her in person. Katherine slumped further in her chair and felt her disappointment deepen. "I understand, Sarah. I really do. If you ever change your mind, please give me a call."

"Thanks, Katherine," Sarah said. "I'll keep that in mind."

They hung up and Katherine sat there for a few minutes, trying to process what had just happened. She felt like she had just been sucker-punched but not by Sarah, she had done this to herself. This was a big program and a big decision for people to make, and she should have made an appointment with Sarah instead of trying to talk to her over the phone. She was going to have to regroup and change her presentation method to be face-to-face, no exceptions.

Katherine spent the next few hours brainstorming ways to get in front of potential candidates who might be interested in the program and developing a two or three-minute pitch that would get people interested in the program, and open to hearing more. Two of the first three candidates had been a result of chance meetings, serendipitous events that weren't planned. She didn't want to rely on luck, she needed a solid plan for how to pitch the program and help people see the value of Wilson's offer.

Katherine finally came up with a strategy and put together a presentation that she felt good about. It was tailored specifically to the needs of her target audience, and it included a way for them to opt-in to receiving more information from her. She was ready to start meeting with people again, and this time she would get the results she wanted.

By bedtime, Katherine was set to put her plan into action. She would make appointments with potential candidates and meet with them in person. This time, things would go much better than they had on the phone.

The old critical thoughts were still with her, but they were quieter than they had been before. Maybe it was because Wilson Devereaux had boosted her confidence or maybe it was her own stubbornness, but Katherine was going to make this work. Sarah had said no, but that didn't mean everyone else she talked with would also say no. Katherine was going to give up. She had a plan, and she was going to see it through. She would get the results she wanted, and then her sister would have no choice but to admit that Katherine was talented and capable. This time, things were going to go her way.

CHAPTER 8

"See you after the game, Mom!" Zoey jumped out of the car and ran towards her teammates, who were already warming up on the soccer field. Katherine watched her go with a smile, feeling grateful that her daughter was so active and loved playing sports. It had been Katherine's dream as a child to play professional soccer, but it wasn't meant to be. She'd had to find other ways to scratch that competitive itch and business had been the perfect outlet.

She walked toward the bleachers on the sidelines, scanning the crowd for friendly faces. Katherine didn't recognize anyone in the bleachers, so she went straight to the sidelines where a group of parents had gathered. The first person she noticed was a man in his mid-30s watching the kids warm-up with a look of intense concentration. He had short, dark hair and was wearing a blue polo shirt and khaki pants.

The man turned his head and their eyes met for a moment. There was something familiar about him, but she couldn't place it. "Hi," Katherine said, approaching the group. "Do you mind if I join you?"

The man turned to look at her and his face softened into a smile. "Katherine, right? Zoey's mom?"

"Yeah," she replied. "I'm sorry, sometimes I'm terrible with names. You are...?"

"Tony Baldwin," he said, holding out his hand. "It's nice to meet you."

Katherine shook his hand, and they exchanged a few words about the game before Tony's attention was pulled away by his daughter. Katherine watched him for a moment, struck by how deeply he seemed to care for his daughter. It was clear that he loved her very much.

The game started and Katherine turned her attention to the field. She cheered for both teams, enjoying the chance to watch her daughter play.

"She's a good player," he said, nodding toward Zoey.

"Thanks, she loves playing soccer." Katherine smiled. Then she gestured toward the soccer field. "Which one is yours?"

He pointed toward a red-headed girl with a ponytail wearing the Tiger's team jersey. "That's my daughter, Emily."

Katherine nodded, her eyes still on the game. "She looks like she knows what she's doing out there."

"She does," Tony replied. "She's been playing for a few years now."

In between cheering for their daughters, they chatted like they'd known each other for much longer than an hour. They soon found out they had a lot in common. They were both from the area, loved to read, and were passionate about their work. Tony offered to buy Katherine a soda from the concession stand and, since it was getting hotter on the sidelines, she accepted.

"So, Tony," Katherine said after they had ordered their drinks, and made their way back to the sidelines. "What do you do?"

He was quiet for a moment before he spoke again. "I'm between careers at the moment. I used to have a couple of movie theaters, but I lost them during the recession."

"I'm sorry to hear that," Katherine said, sympathetically. "That must have been tough."

Tony nodded. "It was. I'm still trying to figure out my next move. I've got a few ideas but nothing solid yet."

"I know it's hard to start over from the bottom of the pile. I've been there, too. When my husband died, I had to shift gears and figure out life without him."

Tony's face softened and he gave her a sad smile. "I'm sorry to hear that. He was young, right?"

Katherine nodded. "Yeah. He wasn't even 40 yet. It was a shock."

They fell into silence for a moment, both lost in their own thoughts. Then Tony spoke again. "So, what do you do, Katherine? For work I mean."

"Funny you should ask, actually," Katherine said, smiling, eager to jump into her newly revised program pitch. "I guess you could say I'm in fund-raising."

"How's that?" he asked, his interest piqued.

"I'm working with real estate expert, Wilson Devereaux, to create a program called the Overnight Millionaire. It's a program that helps people learn the value of growing their wealth. Wilson will give one million dollars to program applicants who submit the best business case for how they would use a gift of one million dollars to grow their wealth. And the proposal can be anything from investing in real estate to building a business. The only thing winners can't do is give the money away to someone else."

"Wow! It sounds like a great idea," Tony said after she had finished speaking. "What's the catch?"

Katherine shook her head. "No catch. Wilson Devereaux just wants to help people grow their wealth so they can live better lives and, hopefully, pay their good fortune forward." She paused a moment letting the information sink in. "In fact, even applicants who aren't chosen will still get one hundred thousand dollars as a consolation prize."

"That's really generous of him," Tony said.

Katherine nodded. "It is. Wilson is a really great guy."

Tony was silent for a moment, clearly considering the offer. Then he spoke again. "Well, I don't know if I have a good business case, since I'm kind of between gigs at the moment, but I'd like to learn more about this."

The parents on the sidelines began to hoot and yell as Tony's daughter got the ball and moved towards the goal. Tony and Katherine were both cheering her on, their voices drowned out by the others.

"Go, baby! Score that goal!" Tony shouted.

"She's so close!" Katherine exclaimed. "And look, Zoey is in a position to assist if Emily needs it."

The girl took a few more steps and then kicked the ball, scoring a goal for the Tigers, putting them ahead of their opponent. The parents on the sidelines went wild, screaming and clapping. Tony and Katherine were the loudest.

"That was an amazing goal!" Katherine said after a few minutes had passed and everyone had calmed down.

Tony nodded. "Yeah, she's been working really hard at practice."

After the game was over, and they said their goodbyes, they exchanged numbers and parted ways. As they walked to the car, Katherine noticed Zoey peering at her quizzically.

"Something wrong, sweetie?" she asked.

"No," Zoey replied. "I'm just wondering why you're smiling. Is it because we won the soccer game?"

"I am very happy your team won, Sweet Pea," Katherine said. "But I'm also smiling because I think I might be able to help someone change their life soon."

"Really?" Zoey asked, her eyes widening in excitement. "So, you scored a goal today, too, huh?"

Katherine laughed. "I guess you could say that."

"I'm so proud of you, Mommy," Zoey replied, skipping alongside her mother. "Good job!"

Katherine hugged her daughter. "I'm proud of you, too, baby. You played a great game today."

And, for the first time that week, Katherine realized she was proud of herself, too. She had taken a big step in her business strategy, and she felt so good about her business pitch. It was short and simple, but she had also presented it with passion and energy and that, she believed made all the difference.

***

Katherine had been riding high on the success of her new business pitch for a couple of days. She and Tony met the day after the soccer game, and he agreed to apply for the program. She felt so good that it boosted her confidence beyond anything she thought was possible, and she felt so much more at ease that she connected with three more people who were at least open to hearing more about the program.

Wilson was ecstatic with the applicants, and that put her on top of the world. She was starting to feel like this was going to be a great opportunity for everyone involved including her. Katherine sat at the lunch counter in a small diner not far from her apartment. She had just finished setting up a meeting with another potential applicant and was now so engrossed in checking email on her phone that she didn't notice the person who sat down next to her until they spoke.

"Excuse me, I don't want to be rude, you look like you're really busy," the young man said. He was young, with dark hair and eyes. He was wearing button-down shirt and slacks, and he looked like he was about to go into an important business meeting. "But I couldn't help but overhear you talking about a business opportunity."

Katherine frowned and put her phone away. He quickly apologized when he saw her expression. "I'm sorry, I didn't mean to eavesdrop."

"No, it's okay," she replied with an easy smile. "I'm the one having business calls in the middle of a diner. It's not like I'm exactly being quiet about it."

"I totally get it," he said. "If you don't mind me asking, what is the business opportunity? You sounded really excited about it and that got my attention."

Katherine filled him in on the Overnight Millionaire Program, and he listened with rapt attention. When she was finished, he leaned back in his seat and let out a low whistle. "Wow. That sounds like an incredible opportunity."

"It is," Katherine replied, finding the conversation exciting that someone approached her about the program. "I'm sorry, I didn't catch your name."

"Oh, sorry," he said, extending his hand. "I'm Charlie Davis."

Katherine shook his hand and smiled. "It's nice to meet you, Charlie. I'm Katherine Johnson."

Charlie nodded and sat up a little straighter in his seat. "So, Katherine, are you the creator of this program?"

"No, I'm not," she replied. "But I am Wilson Devereaux's right-hand gal, and he chose to help find candidates for the program."

"Do you think I could apply?" he asked, and his eyes lit up with excitement. "I'm a student and I really don't have a lot of money, but I've been trying to come up with a way to pay for medical school, and this could be it."

"Oh, you're studying to be a doctor?" She said with an appreciative nod. "That's impressive."

"Not yet. I'm finishing my undergrad degree over the summer, and I'm enrolled in med school for the fall term."

Katherine frowned, her excitement dissipating slightly. "Charlie, I don't want to discourage you, but the program is for people who want to grow their wealth. Unless you want to invest the money somehow or use it to build a business, I'm not sure that going to med school is exactly the same thing as growing your wealth. It usually takes doctors a while to start being profitable. And you don't even have a business yet."

"But that's the beauty of it," he replied quickly. "I can start one. I've been wanting to design and sell custom Print on Demand items like coffee mugs and tee shirts for a while so I can use the money to help pay for school or for living expenses. There's a lot of money to be made in POD. My friend is making ten grand a month from selling coffee mugs and stuff. If I invest in my own business, it would help make my real dream come true. My passion is for healing people. I want to be a surgeon."

Katherine was taken aback by his response. He didn't seem deterred at all by the fact that he didn't have a business yet. In fact, he seemed more committed than ever. "That's really impressive, Charlie. Your enthusiasm is infectious."

He blushed. "Thanks. I really want this, you know? Grad school is really expensive."

Katherine leaned back in her seat and thought about what he said. Charlie had a good business idea, and he was certainly passionate about it. "Okay, Charlie," she said finally, "tell me more. What's the big deal about your Print on Demand business idea and how can it help you grow your wealth?"

He grinned in way that suggested he'd been waiting for the question and was eager to answer it. "Ok, check this out. First, it's a relatively low-cost business to start up. All I really need is a computer and some software for creating images and text for the items I want to print. Second, there's a huge potential for growth. Think about it." he leaned forward, his eyes gleaming with excitement. "It's a flexible business model that I can run from anywhere, I don't have to carry inventory because the supplier will print and ship the items when the order comes through. It's creative and fun, and it's also a recession-proof business. People are always going to need things printed, whether it's business cards, flyers, or custom t-shirts."

"Wow!" Katherine's eyes widened. "I didn't know all that. You really have done your homework."

Charlie nodded. "I did a lot of research before I decided this was the right business for me. I'm confident I can be successful with it. With the right marketing and some hard work, I could quickly start making a lot of sales, and turn the business into a real money-maker."

"Ok, since you've done your homework," Katherine folded her arms on the counter and leaned forward. "Tell about some of the risks involved."

He took a deep breath and shrugged. "The main downside to Print on Demand is that it can be a bit slow to get started.

I need to spend time creating designs and marketing my products before I start seeing any sales come in. And because I won't be carrying inventory, I have to rely on the supplier to print and ship the items promptly, which can sometimes be a challenge. There's also the potential for copyright infringement if I'm not careful about the designs I use. But overall, if I plan this thing right, I think the benefits outweigh the risks."

Charlie outlined the rest of his business plan for Katherine, and she could see the potential in it. Not only was he passionate about it, but he also had a good understanding of the market and what it would take to be successful. He wasn't just winging it; he had put a lot of thought into it.

"I think you have a really great idea, Charlie," she said finally. "And I'm not just saying that. But if it's such an easy way to make money, and doesn't take much to start up, then why do you need one million dollars to get going?"

"Fair point," he agreed. "It may not take much money to start up, but this isn't Field of Dreams. Just because I build it, the customers may not come especially if they can't find my product. You've gotta have some advertising dollars behind you to let people know you exist and that you've got what they're looking for. If I can get a little help with promotion and marketing costs, it will go a long way towards getting the business off the ground."

"I see your point," Katherine said. "And I agree that promotion is important. But I'm not sure Wilson Devereaux is going to give you a million dollars just for opening a printing business."

"He might not," Charlie admitted. "But he's also not going to give it to someone who doesn't have a good plan or who isn't passionate about their idea. I think I have both of those things. Plus, I'm confident in my ability to make this business successful while I'm in school and it will help my dream of becoming a doctor a reality."

Katherine chuckled and shook her head. "You are something else, you know that?"

"I do my best," he grinned.

"Well, I'll tell you what," she said as she got to her feet. She pulled out the information for the website and handed it to him. "Go ahead and fill out the application and we'll take it from there."

"Thank you so much, Katherine," he said, shaking her hand. "I really appreciate your consideration."

"Don't thank me yet," she cautioned. "You still have to impress Wilson Devereaux, but I don't think you're going to have much of a problem doing that."

"I'm going to do my best," he promised. "I'll fill out the application."

"Okay," Katherine said as she headed toward the exit. "I'm excited to see what you put together."

"Thanks, Katherine," he called after her. "I can't believe I ran into you like this. It's kinda surreal, isn't it?"

Katherine stopped a moment and looked back at him. "Yeah, it is. But you never know what's going to happen in life. You just have to be open to the possibilities and believe in yourself. And you, my young friend, have both of those things."

As Katherine walked to her car, she couldn't help but smile. Life was just weird. Sometimes, you had to really work hard to gain just a little bit of ground, and other times, opportunities just fell into your lap. Several days ago, she had been despondent over the lack of candidates for the program and disappointed in her own performance in how she searched for those candidates. And now, here she was, with a promising young man who had come out of nowhere. She wondered what other surprises life had in store for her.

CHAPTER 9

Today's the big day, Katherine thought, the moment she opened her eyes. It's the day of the meeting to decide who of the Overnight Millionaire program would receive one million dollars and learn the value of growing their wealth directly from real estate magnate, Wilson Devereaux. After all the hard work—the ups and downs, successes, and heartaches—she couldn't believe the day was finally here.

Wilson had hand-picked her—taken a chance on her when she didn't even know if she was capable of doing the job. She was ecstatic and scared and felt so many emotions as she got ready for the day, she almost poured coffee in Zoey's morning cereal instead of milk.

In just a few hours, she'd be sitting in a room with one of the richest men in the country, helping him choose who would receive a life-changing amount of money. It felt like something out of a dream. Katherine's inner critic chimed in. *What if you said something wrong? What if you make the wrong decision, or Wilson disagrees with your choices?* He had put so much faith in her, and she didn't want to let him down.

Stop it, she told herself. *You're going to do great. This is your moment, and you're going to make the most of it.*

Katherine took a deep breath and finished getting herself together. Katherine took extra care with her appearance that day, wanting to look her best when she met with Wilson and the other members of the committee. She chose a conservative gray suit and low heels, her hair pulled back into a sleek bun. It was time to show Wilson Devereaux—and her family—what she was made of.

***

She dropped Zoey off at school and drove to Wilson's mansion, arriving a few minutes early. She wanted to get a feel for the other members of the committee and see what kind of people they were. As she walked into the room, she felt like everyone was staring at her. It made her nervous, but she walked over to Wilson who greeted her warmly.

"Katherine! I'm glad you're here," he said, giving her an affectionate hug. "Let me introduce you to everyone."

He went around the room, introducing her to two other people who would be part of the program selection committee: a tall woman called Claire who sported a perfectly coiffed pixie haircut and was dressed in a Chanel suit, and a man named Aaron in a three-piece suit complete with a pocket square tucked into his jacket pocket.

Wilson finally signaled that it was time to begin the meeting. The first order of business was to go over the proposals that had been submitted by the candidates. "As you all know," he said, "We're here to evaluate the proposals and choose the candidates who will receive the seed money, and my guidance, to help each of them to learn the value of investing their money to grow their wealth. I've asked Katherine to join us today because she knows each of these candidates, and I value her opinion. She has a fresh perspective that I think will be most helpful. We'll hear about each candidate first, then make our decisions after lunch."

Katherine nodded at Claire and Aaron and smiled. They smiled warmly in return, and Claire said, "We're excited to hear your thoughts, Katherine." Wilson continued. "The first candidate is Liz Lau, who proposes expanding her business."

"Yes," Katherine said. "Liz coaches young mothers one-on-one on how to start a business while raising their families. She has a real passion for working with young moms who want to be entrepreneurs. She's looking for a way to make her business scalable. There are only so many hours in the day and she can only coach so many people. She can't take on any more clients, and she's having to turn people away."

Claire nodded. "I like that she's recognized that she needs to pivot her business model if she's going to grow her business. That's important."

"I agree," Katherine said. "But she's at capacity with how many clients she can coach. I think with the right resources, she could be even more successful. She wants to train other coaches in her business strategy approach for working with entrepreneurs who are young mothers and provide resources for them so they can coach other people."

"Ok," Aaron said as he read through the proposal "But what does her proposal entail? Does she want to franchise, or will she keep the reins of the business closer to home?"

"To start, she wants to build a team of coaches she will directly support," Katherine said. "She's very keen to ensure quality control for her methods and processes. She's very passionate about her work, and she wants to ensure that the people her consultants are coaching get the same level of quality support that she would provide if they were working with her one-on-one."

Katherine was effusive in praising her personality, drive, passion, and her business acumen.

"There's one other thing I like about Liz," Claire said. "Her business is built not just on making money for herself but also on helping other women succeed in their businesses. I think that's important."

"I agree," Katherine said. "She's not just mission-driven, she's also people-oriented and I think that will help her immensely. If she has the money, she can advertise properly, design the training courses for her new coaches, and give them the support they need."

"Ok," Wilson said, "who's up next?"

"Samuel DeLeon," Katherine said. "I met him in a coffee shop where he works as a barista. I overheard Sam talking to a co-worker about his big dreams. He wants to buy some real estate of his own so he can prove to his father that he can run his own business. And then maybe join the family business, but on his own terms."

"Interesting," Claire said. "What does he propose to do with the money?"

"In the proposal, he lays out a plan to buy and renovate older, beautiful buildings and turn them into desirable showplaces for tenants," Katherine said. "The first building is in a historic district downtown, so there are some restrictions he'll have to navigate. But the historic district is undergoing a renaissance, so it's a perfect time to buy in."

"Who's his father?" Aaron asked, looking up from the proposal.

"Mitchell DeLeon," Claire chimed in, reading from the proposal. "He owns some commercial property in town."

"Ah, like father, like son," Arron nodded.

"Exactly," Katherine said. "Sam's a go-getter. He's not afraid of a little hard work. He's been working on his plans for months, and he's really passionate about it."

"I like that he has a solid plan," Aaron said, "but I'm curious about how much he knows about renovating buildings."

"He's done his research," Katherine said. "He's talked to some contractors his father knows, and he has a realistic idea of the costs and the timeline. He knows it won't be easy, but he's up for the challenge."

"I think he'll need to be," Claire said. "This is a big undertaking."

Wilson chimed in, rubbing his chin thoughtfully. "I like what I see here," he said. "I think Sam has potential. He's got a good head on his shoulders, and he knows what he wants to do. If he can keep his budget in line, he should be able to rent the apartments for a good price."

"I agree," Katherine said. "He's a smart cookie."

"What about his work ethic?" Claire asked with a raised eyebrow. "He sounds like he's motivated, but can he handle the pressure of a real estate project when things get tough?"

Wilson chuckled. "I think that's where I come in," he said. "Real estate is my wheelhouse, and since I'm personally mentoring each participant, I offer my guidance when he needs it. I think with a little of my mentoring, Sam could be a real success."

"There's also his dad," Katherine said. "As long as they get along, he'll have extra support."

"I think this is a good candidate," Wilson said. "What do you think, Claire?"

Claire nodded. "I agree," she said. "I think Sam has potential."

"Ok, let's move on to the next proposal then," Wilson said.

"Billie Palmer," Katherine smiled widely as she said the name. Just the thought of meeting the joyful bakery owner gave her such a warm feeling. "She's amazing."

"You sound like you know her," Claire said with a raised eyebrow. "What does she make?"

"Cupcakes and all kinds of pastries and desserts," Katherine said, enthusiastically. "She makes the most delicious cupcakes you've ever tasted. I read a story about her on the internet and realized her bakery—Sweet Soul Creations—is really close to my house. I took my daughter in to sample a cupcake and we talked to Billie for quite a while. She's so enthusiastic and passionate about her baking."

"How can you go wrong with cupcakes," Claire said with a smile. "We may want to take a little side trip to the bakery at some point."

"I think that can be arranged," Katherine said with a wink. "Anyway, Billie was recently in the news because of her mentoring program."

"What kind of mentoring program?" Aaron asked.

"It started when she studied at Le Cordon Bleu in Paris," Katherine said. "She ran into some financial difficulty with tuition and was awarded one of their scholarships."

"So, she decided to start a program to help other people who are in a tight spot with their education," Aaron said.

"Exactly, but it's more than that," Katherine said. "She's already mentoring two young people in her small bakery, and they've only been open for a little while. Her mentorship program gives young people hands-on experience in a bakery, along with guidance and support to help them launch their own careers."

"That sounds really generous of her," Wilson said. "She's taking on a lot by opening a business and starting a mentoring program at the same time."

"Yeah," Katherine said. "I asked her about that. Billie said that she was always helped by other people when she didn't want to wait to pay it forward. She got a leg up when she needed it most, so she wanted to give other young people the same support."

"That's a really sweet story," Claire replied, clearly moved by Billie's fierce determination and generosity. "What will she do if she gets the one million dollars?"

Katherine smiled even wider. "That's where it really gets good. She wants to expand her bakery so she can take on more mentees," Katherine said. "And maybe open franchises and implement the mentoring model within those stores, as well."

"You've done some great homework on Ms. Palmer," Wilson said, proudly as he looked at Katherine. "I think we have a definite contender."

"She's amazing," Katherine repeated, her eyes shining with admiration for the woman who dreamed big and was working hard to make her dream become reality.

"Ok, who's up next?" Wilson asked as they prepared to read the next proposal.

"I think we're up to Tony Baldwin, now," Aaron said.

Katherine felt her stomach tighten as she prepared to deliver the news about Tony. Wilson Devereaux, Claire, and Aaron looked at her expectantly, waiting for her to continue. "Tony has had some challenges," Katherine said quietly. "He lost his businesses in the economic downturn, and he's having trouble finding his way back. When I spoke to him, he said he had a few ideas for his next business but wasn't sure."

"What kind of businesses did he have?" Claire asked.

"He owned a few movie theaters," Katherine replied. "But they were struggling even before the recession hit."

"So, what's he proposing to do now if we award him the money?" Wilson inquired.

Katherine took a deep breath and met his gaze. "From what he has said in his proposal, he will deposit the money in his stocks and mutual funds and let them grown."

"Ah," Wilson nodded. "Taking the safe route."

"I'm not sure if it's the safe route or the smart route," Katherine said. "Tony is a very smart man, but he seems to have lost his confidence. I think he just needs a push in the right direction, and I believe he has the potential to be a great candidate for this opportunity."

"Well, we'll take a look at his proposal and make a decision," Wilson said. "Anything else?"

Katherine shook her head. "That's all for now," she replied. "I guess we need to discuss the last candidate, Charlie Davis."

"Actually, Charlie didn't submit a full proposal," Aaron said. "And he failed to provide the additional information requested of him by the deadline."

Katherine's heart sank as she realized that Charlie was out of the running not only for the million-dollar prize but the $100,000 runner-up prize as well. "Wow," she said. "That's surprising. He was so excited about submitting a proposal for the program when I chatted with him."

"It's not your fault, Katherine," Wilson said. "He might have been waiting until the last minute to submit something and just didn't have enough time."

Katherine felt terrible for Charlie. He was so excited about trying to win the money and now he was out of the running.

"All right," Wilson said as he gathered up all the proposals. "Thank you all for your participation in this process. Let's take a break for some food—I think our staff has a lovely alfresco lunch set up on the terrace. When we come back, we'll make the final decisions about the candidates."

"What comes next?" Claire asked, rising from her seat.

"How will we inform the participants of our decisions?"

"We're going to throw a big party and a press conference," Wilson grinned and winked at Katherine. "And you're going to be my right-hand woman, helping me make the announcement."

As they walked through the door to the terrace, Katherine's stomach growled in anticipation of the delicious lunch that awaited them. But even more than the food, she was excited about what the future held for the participants of their program. Even though she tried to enjoy the beautiful day and the lovely food, but she couldn't help thinking about Charlie Davis and feeling disappointed that he hadn't made it to the final round. She knew he was down, but she thought he had more fight in him. She was going to keep an eye on him and see if she could help him take advantage of this amazing opportunity when Wilson ran it again. Because if there was one thing she had learned about her new friend, Wilson Devereaux wasn't done changing lives. There would be another round of recruiting for the Overnight Millionaire program, and Katherine couldn't wait to get started.

CHAPTER 10

Two weeks passed and finally, the day of the Overnight Millionaire announcement party arrived. Katherine arrived at Wilson's mansion early to ensure everything was set up for the party and the press conference. The ballroom had been turned into a party venue with tall cocktail tables and hors d'oeuvres served by staff in black attire.

The walls were a cream color with gold trim and deep decorative crown molding. The floor was dark wood that had been polished to a shine. There were several windows along one wall that let in the beautiful natural light. One wall sported floor-to-ceiling bookcases filled with leather-bound books. A fireplace was the focal point of the room, and it had an ornate mantelpiece. French doors led out to a terrace where there was more food, and a string quartet played classical music.

The walls were decorated with beautiful tapestries and antique paintings, and a large crystal chandelier hung from the ceiling. A grand marble staircase led up to a second-floor balcony, and Katherine could see people beginning to arrive and take their seats.

The invitations had requested invited guests and their "plus one" dress in something more formal than business casual attire. So, Katherine wore a simple black dress and heels. She had her hair pulled back in a low ponytail. She accepted a glass of champagne from a passing server and sipped it as she looked around the room. Katherine walked over to one of the windows and looked out at the terrace. The sunlight was shining off the marble floor. There were people milling about and talking. Wilson Devereaux stood a few feet off to the side chatting with a group of people.

When Wilson spotted her, he called out her name and beckoned her over. They were members of the media, the City Council, and the local Chamber of Commerce present. He introduced her as his right-hand woman and the person responsible for finding the participants of their program.

The group chatted for a few minutes about the event, and then Wilson excused himself to speak with someone else. Katherine stayed and talked with the group for a bit longer, before moving on to talk to other people at the party. She heard a woman call her name and turned to see Billie Palmer walking towards her.

"Katherine, it's so good to see you." Billie squealed as she hugged her. "This is so exciting, and I think it's a great sign that I might have been chosen as one of the winners."

"Well, I can't let the cat out of the bag quite yet," Katherine said with a big smile. "But I have a feeling that if you're excited now, you'll be over the moon in a few minutes."

"I just can't believe this is happening," Billie said as she looked around the room. "It still feels like a dream."

"I know," Katherine replied. "But I promise it's all real. It's so great that you were able to fit catering the desserts for this event into your schedule."

"Yeah," her eyes sparkled. "I was just so excited when I got the call. I mean, it's not every day that you get to cater for a soiree where I'm one of the guests. Speaking of which, I think I'll check the dessert table to make sure everything is ok." Billie said before hugging Katherine again and heading toward the terrace.

Katherine scanned the room for other people she knew. She was about to get something to eat when she saw Sam and Liz across the room. They chatted excitedly with a group of people Katherine didn't recognize, she guessed they might be reporters or local politicians.

She started to walk over to them but was intercepted by Tony. "Hello, Katherine," he said with a smile. "It's good to see you."

"Hi, Tony," she replied, giving him a hug. "It's nice to see you too. I'm glad you could make it."

"I'm a little surprised that I got an invitation to this press conference," he said with a laugh. "I didn't think my proposal was all that interesting. You said the program was for anyone who was interested in growing their wealth."

"Yeah, it is."

Tony shrugged sheepishly. "But from overhearing people as they talk, most of the candidates submitted proposals for developing some sort of business. I just wanted to learn how to invest my money so that it would grow, so I submitted that I would invest in stocks and mutual funds. I didn't think that was as newsworthy as starting a new business."

"You never know," her eyes twinkled as she looked at him. "Investing is a great way to grow your wealth, depending on your tolerance for risk, and this wasn't just for people building their businesses." She paused a moment and then asked, "Have you talked to Wilson or Claire about the program?"

"Oh, I've been talking to Claire a lot," he said with a grin. "She's been giving me some tips on how to make my money work for me."

Katherine smiled and nodded. Claire was one of the judges for the program and had offered to help all the participants.

"Just wait until you meet Wilson. He's amazing and he'll really give you some great ideas. But I'm glad to hear Claire gave you some good advice," she said. "Hey, have you met Sam and Liz yet?"

"Not yet," Tony replied. "I don't think I know what they look like."

"Then it's time you guys got acquainted," Katherine said as she linked her arm through his. "They might be a great resource for you in brainstorming your next amazing business idea."

As they walked across the room, Billie came in from the terrace with a tray of cupcakes. She headed straight for Katherine and Tony.

"I brought goodies," she said in a sweet singsong voice as she set the tray down on a nearby table. "I just love these parties."

"Just wait until you taste these," Katherine replied. "Have you met everyone yet?"

"No, not yet," Billie said with a shake of her head. "But I'm looking forward to it."

"Well, let me introduce you to Tony then," Katherine said as she turned to him. "Tony, this is Billie. She owns the best cupcake shop in town." Then she motioned for Sam and Liz to join them and made the rest of the introductions.

"Those cupcakes look delicious," Sam said. "They're so beautiful and definitely don't look like they came from a grocery store bakery. I'll bet they're even gourmet flavors."

"You bet," Billie said, enthusiastically. "Let's see, we have Double Chocolate with Cream Cheese Frosting, Salted

Caramel with a Brown Sugar Streusel, Coconut Lime with a White Chocolate Frosting, and my personal favorite is the Pecan Pie cupcake. It has a Vanilla Cake base with a Pecan Pie Filling and a Brown Sugar Buttercream Frosting."

"Mmm," Liz said. "I might have to try one of each."

"I'll second that," Tony said.

Billie gave him an appreciative smile and said, "I'm sure there's more than enough. Have as many as you like."

The conversation continued as they all talked and got to know each other better. Katherine was happy that everyone seemed to be getting along and enjoying themselves.

Wilson's voice over the loudspeaker interrupted them and he asked everyone to take their seats. When everyone was seated, he began to speak.

"Ladies and gentlemen, thank you all for coming today. It is my great pleasure to introduce you to the Overnight Millionaire program. This program was created to help people in our community learn how to grow their wealth and achieve their financial goals."

There was a round of applause from the audience and Wilson continued. "It's important for adults to grow their wealth in order to provide for their families and future generations. As my right-hand person reminded me at the start of this endeavor," he glanced at Katherine and smiled, "it's not just important to build your own wealth, it's also important to find others to whom you can pay your good fortune forward and I'm delighted to say that, with this program, we have a number of applicants whose business proposals included methods of giving back to the community."

Another round of applause erupted from the audience and Wilson continued. "This is a life-changing opportunity for these entrepreneurs and I'm excited to see what they'll do with their awards. Before we get down to the financial awards, I want to introduce you to some people who were instrumental in helping me to create this program and get it off the ground."

He introduced Claire and Aaron, and they stood up to acknowledge the applause. Wilson continued, "Claire runs one of my businesses and was a member of the committee that helped us review all of the proposals. And Aaron, as many of you know, is another of my key advisors. He has been instrumental in helping me grow my wealth, and I'm grateful to have him on my team."

Another round of applause, and Wilson continued. "Next, I want to introduce you to my right-hand person in this endeavor, Katherine Johnson. I met Katherine when she worked at Bright Futures, the non-profit small business support organization for which I am one of the trustees. When I looked at Katherine and her dedication and commitment to helping others, I knew she would be the perfect person to help me find candidates for this program." He paused and gazed proudly at her. "Without Katherine's dedication and hard work, this program would not be possible."

The audience erupted in applause once again, and Katherine felt her cheeks flush with pleasure as she rose to acknowledge the praise with a small, almost embarrassed wave. She was touched by Wilson's words and grateful for the opportunity to have worked with him on such an important project. She felt like a new person.

More applause rang out, and Wilson said, "Now, let's get down to business. There are two award levels for the Overnight Millionaire program. The first is a $100,000 runner-up award for any applicant who presented a business plan that increased their wealth on a basic level. I'm proud to award the first runner-up award to Tony Baldwin for his business plan to grow his wealth through investing in the markets."

Tony's eyes went wide, and he looked genuinely surprised at receiving an award at all. He stood up to accept the prize with shaking hands. Tony took the award, shook Wilson's hand, and smiled for the cameras. He still looked a little shell-shocked as he made his way back to his seat.

As the applause died down, Wilson launched into the next program winner. "The second level of the award is a 1-million-dollar grand prize for the best proposals that increased a person's wealth while helping other people achieve their dreams and financial goals. The money could be used for a business or any other type of larger investment opportunity. I'm proud to award the first grand prize to Liz Lau for her business proposal to expand her current coaching program for young entrepreneurs who are also mothers of young children."

Liz looked stunned as she rose to accept her award. There were more handshakes, pats on the back, and smiling for the cameras. She thanked Wilson and the committee members for their support before returning to her seat. There was a murmur of excitement from the audience as people realized that there were two more awards to give out.

"Next," Wilson said. "We have Samuel DeLeon. Now, I must admit this one is close to my heart because, as a real estate guy, I love to see people who are passionate about property investing rewarded for their hard work. Samuel's business proposal is to renovate the buildings in our town's historic district and turn them into apartments to provide a better place for residents to live and, at the same time, better the neighborhood and community. This project will revitalize an important section of our town and the small business owners who have shops and boutiques in the area stand to benefit from the increased foot traffic. I'm proud to award Samuel with the one-million-dollar grand prize."

Sam jumped out of his seat with a whoop. There were more handshakes, backslapping, and photos as Samuel made his way to the stage to accept his award. He gave a short speech thanking Wilson and the committee members for the opportunity before making his way back to his chair.

The audience was on its feet, clapping and cheering as Wilson prepared to announce the final winner. "And last but not least," he said with a smile, "We have Billie Palmer, who makes the best cupcakes and gourmet pastries and desserts in town. In fact, her bakery, Sweet Soul Creations, catered the dessert tables for our function today, and I know you've all been enjoying those sweet treats all morning."

There was a murmur of agreement from the audience, and Wilson continued. "There's more to Billie than just great desserts, however. She has just opened her first store and also launched the first of many mentoring programs. She gives young people between the ages of 18 and 25 an opportunity to learn all aspects of baking and running a catering business, and she prepares them for a bright future in the industry. Her proposal is a business plan for franchising her bakery and rolling out her mentorship program nationwide. I'm proud to award Billie the 1-million-dollar grand prize."

Billie's mouth dropped open, and she stared at Wilson in disbelief. She couldn't believe that she had actually won an award. There were tears in her eyes as she made her way to the stage to accept her prize. She gave a tearful speech thanking Wilson and the committee members for their support before going back to her seat.

As the applause died down, Wilson said, "Before we end the formal portion of today's program, I'd like to invite Katherine Johnson up to say a few words. She was instrumental in finding these wonderful candidates, and it's only fitting that she gets a chance to say a few words."

Katherine blushed as she made her way to the podium. Wilson hugged her, and she turned to the microphone. "First, I need to thank Wilson for inviting me to share in this amazing journey and for believing in me when I had difficulty believing in myself. I also want to thank the committee members, Claire, and Aaron, for their hard work and dedication in selecting these amazing finalists. And finally, I want to congratulate all the winners on this incredible achievement. You all have worked so hard, and it's so gratifying to see your dreams come true."

Katherine's voice choked with emotion, and there was a loud round of applause before she addressed Liz, Sam, Billie, and Tony. "I'm so proud of all of you," she said. "I've learned so much about the strength and power of the human spirit and how resilient people are in the face of challenging circumstances. All of you exemplify that strength and resilience. And I know that this is only the beginning. These awards are just the start of great things for all of you. Not only that, but it's a great beginning to a program that will continue to change people's lives. Thank you all for coming. This has truly been one of the most satisfying moments of my professional life, and I'm very grateful and humbled to be here."

Katherine learned a lot from Wilson about how to help people value growing their wealth. She helped him understand that including the desire to help others achieve financial and personal goals as you grow your wealth was just as significant.

As they mingled with the local politicians, business owners, and media, guests congratulated the winners and posed for pictures. "This has been an amazing day," Katherine said as she linked her arm through Wilson's. "Thank you for giving me the chance to be a part of it."

Wilson smiled down at her. "It's been my sincere pleasure, Katherine. I knew you'd do a wonderful job, and I think we have the start of a great partnership." he hesitated a moment then said, "Ready to go again?"

"I thought you'd never ask," Katherine's eyes shimmered with gratitude and excitement. "Just say when."

Wilson chuckled and squeezed her shoulder. "When." They both laughed. "Seriously, take a couple of days off to spend time with Zoey and get some rest. Next week, we'll meet to strategize about following up on progress from this first Overnight Millionaire cohort, and then we'll start planning for the next one."

Katherine nodded, her mind already whirring with plans and possibilities. She couldn't wait to get started. She pulled her phone out of her pocket and said to their group of winners. "Hey everyone, I think we need a commemorative group photo to mark this amazing day."

They all gathered around, grinning from ear to ear, and one of the guests snapped the picture for them. Katherine gazed at the image and knew it represented more than just a day's victory. This was the beginning of a movement, and she was thrilled to be a part of it.

After a moment's reflection, she tapped out a short message to her sister, Deirdre, and her mother and father and included the photo with the caption— *First winners of the Overnight Millionaire program with me and millionaire real estate investor Wilson Devereaux. Just you wait. This is only the beginning.*

CHAPTER 11 – ONE YEAR LATER

As with any investment, there is always risk and opportunity. The same is true for our investors.

Tony Baldwin received the runner-up prize of $100,000. His approach to wanting the money in conservative stocks and mutual funds stood in the way of receiving the $1 million award. At the end of one year, following another dip in the market, Tony lost half his investment, and it will take time to recover from that loss.

Liz Lau grew her $1 million to $1.2 million and has expanded her reach to more than 300 coaches nationwide. She has invested wisely in the growth of her business and while her gains seem modest, the future is bright for this talented entrepreneur.

Billie Palmer fulfilled her dreams for her bakery business. She opened up two more bakeries in neighboring cities and doubled the size of her original store. Even after the expansion expenses, she was able to increase the original gift by one hundred fifty percent to $1.5 million.

Sam DeLeon was the big winner. He grew his $1 million to $2.5 million. He did a cash out refinance and gave 100% of investor money back, maintained the property for cash flow and reinvested that cash back into two more properties. He then partnered with his dad to create a mentoring program to teach other people how to syndicate apartments just like he did.

Wilson Devereaux was so thrilled with the results, he had Katherine identify a dozen new recipients for the Overnight Millionaire Program and his vision of teaching people how to make money work and grow became a reality.

As a bonus, Wilson gave Katherine $1 million and coached her personally on how to invest in multifamily real estate. The principles he taught included the benefit of:

- Cash Flow – net income after you subtract all expenses and mortgage from the rental income

- Appreciation – property values go up while tenants pay down the debt

- Tax Benefits – incentives given to investors to purchase real estate

- Multifamily dwellings are one of the strongest assets to have during a recession. He was quick to point out that segment of the real estate market fared the best during the 2008 crash.

- Hedge against inflation – as costs go up, so do property values and rent.

EPILOGUE

We hope you enjoyed this book, we had a lot of fun writing it. Our goal was to pique your interest in real estate investing and get you hungry to learn more about it. For those of you who would like to partner with us on future investment opportunities or learn more about our company, visit: **https://verticalstreetventures.com**

At Vertical Street Ventures, we help

- Our investors – we give them a way to achieve passive income and generate cash flow, build generational wealth for their families

- Our residents/communities we invest in – we make these properties cleaner and safer for our residents. We build the community with events, and give back via our services events including goodie bags, backpack programs, etc.

Here's what a few of our investors have to say:

"I've loved learning how to create a passive income stream with Vertical Street Ventures. It's been refreshing to not rely solely on my job for a salary."

- Gillian

***

"Vertical Street created a passive income stream for my family and it forever changed how we thought about investing in Real Estate."

— Steve

***

"After decades of investing in the equities markets, the Vertical Street team has shown me how to create cash flow through investing in multi-unit apartments."

— Neal

***

We were both able to accelerate our learning in this industry and retire from our corporate jobs sooner than we had anticipated, which was wonderful! We couldn't have done it without the mentors and coaches we had. If you're interested in becoming a more active investor and operator (do what we do), then visit our Academy page. We launched a hands-on mentorship program designed to get you fast tracked in the apartment syndication space. Visit: **https://verticalstreetventures.com/Academy** for more information.

Here's what our current students are saying:

"Ever since we first joined the academy, within our first month we got our first deal!"

— Diana

***

"I would highly recommend it. The hands-on experience, the education you're gonna get from this are so valuable."

- Chris

***

"This academy will really help people get a leg up and get in that first deal via a springboard to move forward in this industry."

- Greg

***

"Our coaches are the best in the industry."

- Louie

Whatever you decide to do next, here's one piece of advice. Just do it. Many people we know consume knowledge but take no action and wonder why they aren't going anywhere. Just do it.

Good luck on your journey to your #lifebydesign.

ABOUT THE AUTHORS

Jenny Gou, Managing Partner

Jenny is a Managing Partner at Vertical Street Ventures, which was established to help individuals achieve their financial goals through passive investing in real estate. She focuses on Business Strategy and execution of the business plan as well as managing relationships and communications with investors.

Prior to becoming a full-time Operator and Investor, Jenny was a Sales Director at Procter & Gamble for 13 years working on brands such as Dawn, Cascade and Swiffer. She managed cross-functional teams on top accounts which included Costco, Walmart, Target, and more. Her overall experience in leading teams, strategy and project management enables Vertical Street Ventures to be the best in industry and make our communities a better place to live.

Jenny graduated from the University of Arizona with a degree in Business Management and received her MBA from the University of Minnesota. She is married to her husband Ronnie and has 2.5 kids (furry one included).

Steven Louie, Managing Partner

Steven is a Managing Partner at Vertical Street Ventures, where he is responsible for acquisitions, sourcing capital, and building key strategic partnerships. He focuses his time on revenue-generating activities for the firm through Multifamily real estate acquisitions.

Steven worked his corporate career in the Benefits / Consulting industry where he held various executive and sales leadership roles at Mercer and MetLife. As a Partner at Mercer, Steven was the Southern CA Office Leader for Mercer's Health, Wealth, and Human Capital Consulting practices. Prior to Mercer, he worked for 16 years at MetLife, where he led the organization in Group Institutional Sales as a Client Executive and a Sales Leader. Steven started his career as a group insurance underwriter and graduated with a Finance degree from California State University, Fullerton.

He has grown his Multifamily portfolio to over 2,500+ units across 4 states (AZ, CA, FL, TX) and has a keen focus on acquisitions and building key partner relationships across the market. In his spare time, he enjoys the "need for speed" as he shifts gears around a race track. Steven also enjoys vacationing with his wife, Rebecca, and two daughters.